KU-438-970

TELETALK

A Dictionary of Broadcasting Terms

BBC Television Training

First published in 1991 by
BBC Television Training
BBC Elstree Centre
Clarendon Road
Borehamwood
Hertfordshire

Printed by BBC Print Unit
Evesham, England

FOREWORD

About two years ago, in an idle moment in the office, I began to worry about some of the language used in a new series of guidelines on video working and tape standards released in the BBC. I say 'worry' because I understood about one word in three and found that my comprehension was so lacking that I did not understand wholly what the new working practices alluded to were likely to involve. This, in the way of all television producers (who tend to approach subjects in a crab-wise manner), led me to thinking of the extent to which I really understood — or could define the television terminology I had been prone to use in the previous twenty years. My conclusions, based on random examples, were not very convincing. A further discussion with Peter Jarvis, the author and progenitor of this glossary, led to the realisation that I was not alone in my thinking.

What should be made clear is that this glossary does not pretend to be definitive or, in the researched and honed style of dictionaries, balanced, neutral and one-hundred percent precise. The method of acquiring terms has, in the main, been to listen to the language of television people, to invite contributions from the many who pass through a training department and to monitor usage in a range of technical and other publications. The starting point for definitions has always been 'experts' (dangerous word) in a given discipline. Occasionally, it can be seen that levity (and even asperity) have been allowed to creep into our definitions. After all, with a language such as that used in film and television, too great seriousness is surely not in order... On the other hand, it is to be hoped that what appears in the following pages will be of positive help to those — especially newcomers — whose life is likely to be spent at least in part, in television in the next few years.

GORDON CROTON
Head of BBC Television Training

PREFACE

I work at the BBC Television Studios at Elstree. Like any other busy studio complex it has its fair share of visitors, some informed but most just curious.

For a long time I had noticed a pattern. The visitor would begin all brimming with curiosity, eagerly pouring out questions. We would move smartly from film to editing suite, to studio gallery to construction workshop to projection theatre. Along the way there would be interruptions from colleagues asking about scripts, or locations, or problems with laboratories. Rapidly the visitor's eyes would glaze over. Most of our guests were understanding not one sentence in ten of all that they heard.

An answer seemed to offer itself in the form of a glossary outlining all the basic terminology of television. It was something that the BBC Television Training could put together in a few weeks and ought to take the form of a slim booklet. It was envisaged as a pamphlet of around ten or so pages, probably in fairly large print for the slow readers of the industry, and larded with diagrams to fill up the empty spaces.

Many months later we have come up with this volume. It is certainly incomplete and, by the time you are reading it, a range of additional terminology will probably have developed. As the list of terms grew and grew, I became increasingly aware that we, the television professionals, don't just have access to a few words of jargon. We speak a complete language.

Imagine that our bemused visitor ends his tour of the studios by seeking a stiff drink. Around the bar of the BBC Club stand knots of various professionals themselves. Let us say that there is one group of transmitter engineers, one party of actors, a gang of newsroom journalists, a few film sound recordists and some designers who are discussing computer graphics. If the visitor eavesdrops on each conversation in turn he might conclude that Broadcasting is a new Babel. These people talk dialects as different as Urdu and Greek.

Yet, in reality, all these people have to work together and communicate freely. To do so they do what the tribes of Nigeria and New Guinea do. They switch to a *lingua franca*. Television people talk Tele-pidgin.

All languages are worth studying, they tell you a lot about the peoples who speak them. In the beginning there were engineers and engineers begat radio and radio begat television and the engineers saw that it was good. The engineers spoke a technical tongue which in its pure form is still a secret tongue understood by themselves alone. They invented television but they needed something more exciting than a test card to put in front of their cameras (there are engineers who find looking at test cards a reward in itself but the paying public is less enthusiastic)!

And so in there came the performers with their own language and traditions. They came from the theatre and the music hall.

The language spoken on a film stage or in a television rehearsal room would be quite familiar to Mr Vincent Crummles and the strolling players who met Nicholas Nickleby. It is a world of wardrobe and green rooms and postiche and properties. It is a world where drapes are swagged, rostra are set in and flats are flown.

Artistes move up and down stage and sometimes camp it up and upstage each other. At their worst they miss their cues and dry, while the rest of the cast corpses. Otherwise, they hit their marks and make their exits left and their entrances right, without a prompt, just as their forefathers did on the stage of Shakespeare's Globe Theatre.

The end of the 1950's brought changes. A new generation of lightweight film equipment became available. Directors were no longer trapped by the walls of the electronic studio. Now everyone had to learn the language of the film industry and the jargon of Hollywood. Lenses became described in focal lengths instead of angles of view, tripods replaced pedestals, life revolved around shoots and rushes, cutting rooms and dubbing theatres, show prints and opticals.

And along with the film crews came another horde of invaders, from the failing photo journals and magazines of the period and from Fleet Street.

The language of actors evokes footlights and leading ladies, and that of the film folk Eisenstein and Sunset Boulevard. The dialect of the Newsroom evokes images of green eye shades and dirty whisky glasses, brimming ashtrays, thundering headlines, front pages held, sleazy court cases and true confessions. For the hacks, good stories are hard stories. They break, or are scooped, or subbed, or spiked, or torn from the rip-and-read, and sent to the morgue. Victims are staked out or doorstepped.

These are the four main roots of our tongue; engineering, the stage, the film industry and the newspaper office. But there are many borrowings from elsewhere. Graphic designers have brought us the argot of the illustrator and the publisher. The all-conquering computer makes us live in a world of interfaces and scratchpads and VDUs. Commercial television has absorbed the language of the advertising agency. Satellite television gives us words from the Space Race, and the world of pop music has not only given us a new form, the pop video, but with it the racy slang of the roadie and record producer. I'm particularly taken with their name for the creature who has disrupted more location shoots than I care to recall — the Jobsworth.

All very interesting you might say, but why should anyone need this sort of book? Outsiders don't need to know and insiders seem to pick up the lingo without difficulty.

Then just imagine that you have decided to give your children a treat and take them to the shoot of an L.E. Series on the Lot where you find half the Hoofers Corpsing because the Gaffer has fallen off the Elephant's Foot trying to fix a Brute that just blew a Bubble while the Sound Recordist has Frying on his Cans due to a set of duff Cannons and needs a Sex Changer. No wonder that when the next Slate is In The Can the Director has told the P.M. that he's Calling A Wrap as soon as he's Busked a final Take on The Legs, and will sort it out in the Off-line. So you think you speak Telly?

I have found some problems insoluble. Many television terms have different meanings in different parts of the industry. Every professional who has been penned into a corner at a party and asked to come up with a clear distinction between the director and the producer will recognize the problems. Definitions tend to start with 'well, you see, it all depends...'. Role titles are particularly variable. The jobs done by an assistant floor manager in the BBC are covered by a stage manager in the independent company next door. A facilities company making commercials might expect a second assistant director to do the job and in a big feature film a range of operatives will be responsible — properties masters and assistants, runners, best boys and so on. In the BBC there are differences of usage between departments and between London and the regions.

These differences are as nothing compared to the chasm between the British and American uses of English. American broadcasting grew out of a very different process from the British. It invented a language peculiar unto itself, with working practices very unlike ours. Even everyday words like 'talent' and 'remote' have quite different connotations in the United States, and the word 'gallery' for a studio control room is incomprehensible across the Atlantic. I have attempted to cover the commonest American usages in this book. Otherwise the forms and spelling are all British English.

Few technical definitions are comprehensive enough for my engineering colleagues. If there has been any conflict of interest I have usually gone for clarity and intelligibility against detail and qualification. There are no lack of technical manuals covering different subjects in depth for those who wish to enquire further. To keep the book within bounds I have tried to limit myself to the terms most likely to be heard from engineers by producers and directors.

Finally, I must apologize to the many manufacturers of equipment whose names, and whose products, have been omitted. They may gnash their teeth as, I imagine, do manufacturers of domestic equipment who find that English housewives invariably talk about 'doing the hoovering' and French ones call any kind of refrigerator a frigidaire.

Broadcasters blithely and regularly adopt trade names and incorporate them into the jargon with variable degrees of accuracy. There are many kinds of rub-down lettering other than Letraset and different prompting devices than Autocue, but the words have become generic. My selection is probably quixotic and based upon the terms which have become most common during my BBC career.

But then, as I began by saying, we had to stop somewhere. Anyone who feels significantly slighted by my omissions, should write to us. There may, one day, be a second edition.

PETER JARVIS
Senior Instructor, Film
BBC Television Training

BBC Television Training
wishes to thank all those in
the BBC radio and television services,
the IBA companies and
the Independent and Corporate Television Sectors
who have contributed to this book.

Production Secretary	Georgie Liddle
Word Processing	Sandie Taylor
Technical Advisers	Ken Angold-Stephens
	Bill Bell
	Ed Boyce
	Dave Buckley
	Dick Burden
Comedy & Dance Consultant	Mike Crisp
Current Affairs Consultant	Mike Catherwood
Studio Production Adviser	Brian Phillips
Research	Kathy Chater
Design & Production	Shirley Greenfield
Graphics	Nick Skelton
General Editor	Gordon Croton
Compiled by	Peter Jarvis

EDITOR'S NOTE

Editing this work has not been easy. The definitions were less of a problem than how to arrange them. For various reasons, too long and boring to go into here, the following decisions were made:

1) Initials — and how the industry loves them — are listed at the beginning of each section of the alphabet, where they are written out in full. If this does not provide sufficient explanation, the diligent scholar is then referred to the full version within the main body of each section.

2) Within each section all definitions beginning with a single word are listed first in alphabetical order, then hyphenated words and finally compound words without a hyphen. Thus **fish skin** is followed by **fish-eye** and then **fishpole**.

3) Numerals are written in words, e.g. 525 appears as **five-two-five**.

Occasionally, it was not possible to find out how a word was actually spelled and in these cases I have gone with the majority decision, e.g. **barron box**. This originally theatrical term was one many people knew but had never seen written down. Further research may yet give a definitive answer and this and other errors will be corrected in any future edition there may be.

KATHY CHATER

A/B Script abbreviation for **as before**, to indicate repeat use of a previous shot.

ABC 1. American Broadcasting Company. **2.** Australian Broadcasting Commission. **3.** Associated British Cinemas. One-time main distributor of films in the UK.

ABS See **Association of Broadcasting Staff**.

AC See **alternating current**.

ACTT See **Association of Cinematograph and Television Technicians**.

AD See **assistant director**.

ADO See **Ampex digital optics**.

ADR See **automatic dialogue replacement**.

AFM See **assistant floor manager**.

AFNOR See *Association Française de Normalisation*.

AFP See **axial front projection** or *Agence France Presse*.

AGC See **automatic gain control**.

AI See **appreciation index**.

AIBD See **Asia-Pacific Institute for Broadcasting Development**.

AIDA See **Angenieux image diffusion attachment**.

AP See **assistant producer** or **Associated Press**.

ASA See **American Standardisation Authority**.

ASBU See **Arab States Broadcasting Union**.

ASM See **assistant stage manager**.

AST See **autoscan tracking**.

A-V See **audio-visual**.

A Note above middle C to which an orchestra traditionally tunes.

A certificate movie Pre-1970 classification

A feature

by British Board of Film Censors indicating a film suitable for adult audiences. Children up to the age of 16 had to be accompanied by an adult.

A feature Term originating in 1930's cinema when a double bill programme was shown, the 'A' picture being the main attraction with a shorter, cheaper 'B' picture as support.

A mount A form of bayonet lens fitting.

A side The tracks on the side of a gramophone record expected to be the most commercially successful. See **flip side**.

A wind Single perforation 16mm film where the perforations face towards you when the emulsion faces inwards and the film unwinds clockwise.

A & B printing A method for producing film mixes and various optical effects by chequerboarding a film, i.e. cutting alternative negative sequences with overlaps and opaque spacing on two separate rolls of film.

A & B roll working A way of cutting film on two rolls with sequences alternating and with overlaps to allow telecine to mix or to perform other effects without the expense and time needed for laboratory optical effects.

Aatelon A piece of equipment which enables Aaton film cameras to lock on to an electronic monitor and avoid revealing the frame bars, i.e. to film the pictures on a TV screen.

Aaton A Danish manufacturer of film equipment, particularly a camera favoured by current affairs cameramen.

Abekas A digital effects system for manipulating video pictures.

aberration An optical lens defect.

above the line Also known as **over the line** costing. The part of a production which relates to cash costs such as artists fees, film stock, etc, but excluding the cost of resources like studios and staff salaries which are **below the line** costs. See also **convertibility**.

abrasion Scratch mark on a film.

absorption Loss of light passing through an optical system. See **transmission**.

absortion filter A lens filter designed to block certain light wavelengths and transmit others.

abstract film Type of art film in which symbolic or surreal images and sounds are used to convey the director's message without recourse to intelligible narrative. A favourite with art college students and currently undergoing a revival with the arrival of computer-generated graphics. See **video artists**.

academic editing (USA) See A and B roll printing, also called **invisible cutting**.

academy aperture/frame Standard frame size for 35mm film on a ratio of 1.33:1.

academy mole Standard large motorised camera crane developed by the American Motion Picture Research Council. Usually known as a **mole** or **MPRC mole**.

academy standards (USA) Technical film industry standards as defined by the Academy of Motion Picture Arts and Sciences.

accelerated motion Slow motion, so called as, in order to achieve slow motion on projection, the camera motor has to be speeded up during shooting. Sounds illogical but nevertheless true.

acceptance angle The total angle of the cone of rays allowed by a lens to convey an image to an electronic tube or a film surface.

access television Television programmes in which editorial control is offered to non-broadcasting organisations or to members of the public.

acetate Non-inflammable base for film, also known as **safety film/base**. Replaced highly dangerous nitrate base film for professional use in the 1950's. Generally used term to describe all types of safety film whether or not cellulose acetate is the base material.

achromatic lens Lens corrected for chromatic aberrations, giving the same results for all wavelengths (colours).

Acmade A British manufacturer of a range of film cutting room equipment.

Acmiola A film editing machine made by Acmade.

acoustic 1. (adjective) Relating to sound. **2.** (noun) The characteristic sound quality of any location. Every room has its own acoustic, as the surfaces of all materials selectively absorb and reflect different frequencies of sound.

acoustic backing Sound-absorbent material used to regulate the acoustics in theatres and recording studios.

acoustic feedback See **howl around**.

acoustic screen Moveable screens of sound-absorbent or reflective characteristics used in radio or music recording studios to modify sound quality.

action! Command by director to announce that a shot is to begin.

action props Properties such as umbrellas, cigarette lighters, guns, etc, which are used in vision by performers. Distinct from dressing props, which adorn a set, or personal props, which embellish a costume.

action replay The process, often used on sports programmes, of replaying an action in real time or slow motion immediately after the event.

action still A publicity still blown up direct

from a frame of negative or a film as distinct from a specially-shot photograph.

action track (USA) See **image trail**.

active satellite Communications satellite which can receive and re-transmit telecommunication messages.

Acton Hilton Ironic reference to a complex of BBC West London rehearsal rooms.

actualités French term, originally for documentary material, but more specifically used for TV news and current affairs.

actuality 1. Programmes or sequences showing unrehearsed topical events. **2**. A system of claiming expenses in which all bills are submitted as opposed to the recipient claiming a fixed daily allowance.

actuality sound Real sound recorded at the time of filming as opposed to post-sync sound added later at a film dub.

acutance Measurement of the sharpness of a photographic image.

ad lib Improvised speech which does not appear in the script.

adaptation Transformation of an original work such as a stage play, novel or biography into a film or television screenplay: the connection between the two is frequently tenuous.

adapter ring Attachment to a lens converting its original fitting so that it can fit into a different camera body, e.g. a bayonet fitting for a camera designed for screw-fitting lenses.

additive colour Method of colour repro- duction where all the colours in an image are created by the mixing of the three primary colours, red, blue and green. All three in equal quantities make white. Film and TV images are made this way.

additive mix Vision mix where picture sources combine together to produce an overall composite image. Non-additive mix takes only the brightest parts of the two pictures to produce final composite image.

adult viewing Programmes containing explicit sex, gratuitous violence or bad language which are boring only to adults.

advance 1. The distance between picture and sound on a film printed as comopt or commag. The sound track is always printed ahead of the picture for projection. The normal distance is 20 frames for 35mm and 28 frames for commag and 26 frames for comopt 16mm film. In TV also used to describe the distance between the sound and video heads on a recorder. **2.** Money taken out in advance of expenses.

advent TV projector which can front-project any video source on to a screen in studio.

advertising film Obsolete term for a cinema or television commercial.

aerial Antenna for receiving or sending transmitted signals.

aerial camera Type of special effects camera.

aerial platform General name for high camera platform, otherwise known as a **Simon hoist** or **cherry picker**.

aerial shot A picture taken from an aeroplane or from a fixed high position.

afterglow Persistence of glow on a television screen due to the finite decay time of the phosphor coating on the screen.

Agence France Presse (**AFP**) The leading French news agency.

agency tape Written material received on a newsroom news agency teleprinter. See **rip-and-read**.

agent Manager employed by actors, musicians, writers, etc, who acts as intermediary with film, TV companies, etc, to negotiate contracts and fees. See **Mister Ten Percent**.

Agfa-Gevaert A Belgian manufacturer of film stock and photographic materials.

Agfacolour Colour film stock manufactured by Agfa.

agitation Means of cleaning away spent developer from the emulsion in continuous development processes.

air knife Compressed air jets used to clean film during continuous development processes.

airtime Time allocated for a programme's transmission.

aleatory film Film buff term for filming in which the camera is used to observe an actual event without attempting to structure the form in the hope that innate meaning will emerge: from the Latin *aleator*, a dice thrower. A plausible justification for a director who doesn't know what he's doing. See **winging it**.

all singing all dancing Description of any obviously extravagant programme or presentation. See **production number, over the top**.

alpha numeric Video display of numerals and/or words. See **light-emitting diode** and **liquid crystal display**.

alternating current (AC) Electric current in which the polarity is reversed at regular intervals or cycles. In most of the world this is at 50 Hz whilst in North America it is at 60 Hz.

alternator A machine for generating AC current, e.g. for lighting on location.

ambience The total atmospheric value of a scene created by the combination of sound, lighting and set design.

ambient sound The general background sound on location which is extraneous to the sound specifically required for the recording. Constant background atmosphere sound.

ambulance chasing Journalistic technique of following up activities of police, fire, ambulance and the emergency services in the hope of finding a scoop. Sometimes achieved by intercepting police radio.

am dram Amateur theatricals.

American Broadcasting Company (ABC) (USA) One of the major USA networks.

American shot Term used in many countries to describe a mid-shot in which a presenter is cut off at knee level. In UK regarded as an ugly composition and rarely seen.

American Standardisation Authority (ASA) Best known for a scale used to indicate film speed or sensitivity to light. Now the ISO (International Standardisation Organisation) rating is more commonly quoted.

Ampex An American manufacturer of VT recording, video switching and effects equip- ment.

Ampex digital optics (ADO) Digital effects generator manufactured by Ampex.

amplifier Electrical circuit which increases the power of a signal without changing its quality.

amplitude modulator The addition of a low frequency signal to a carrier signal of a higher frequency causing the size of the carrier signal to vary in sympathy with the lower frequency.

analogue recording The recording of a sound or picture signal where the signal being recorded is stored as a continuously variable quantity (e.g. magnetic flux) on the recording medium.

anamorphic A lens system which compresses

a film laterally when being shot but then expands it on projection to give a wide screen cinema format picture such as Cinemascope.

anastigmat A term used for high-quality lenses free from distortion across the frame both vertically and horizontally.

Anchor, Alpha Numeric Character Generator simple form of electronic character generator used mainly for superimposing name captions.

anchorman/woman Presenter in a magazine-style show who introduces and links interview, film and videotape items.

Angenieux A French manufacturer of equipment, particularly camera lenses.

Angenieux image diffusion attachment (AIDA) Attachment for electronic cameras.

angle Journalistic approach to a subject setting out to impose or invent a simple narrative or story line where none is immediately apparent. See **hook.**

angle of view The horizontal angle of a lens which defines the limits of a scene.

Anglia British IBA TV company serving the Eastern counties of England.

animate! Instruction given by a studio director for a movement to occur on a caption or computer graphic.

animated lighting Lighting involving the apparent movement in shot of lamps or filters, e.g. a fire flicker effect, cloud shadows or water reflections.

animatic Advertising agency term for a videotaped pilot for a commercial, usually shot from the storyboards without full animation or live action.

animation Apparent movement of inanimate objects or graphics made by taking a series of single frame shots on film or by using computer techniques to give movement to artwork.

animatronics The use of mechanical or electronic controls in puppetry or models.

announcer The person who reads announcements or trails between programmes on transmission.

answer print The first and subsequent prints from a cut negative submitted by a film processing laboratory to a film editor and director for approval. If corrections are needed, the print will be returned to the laboratory with comments and further corrected antagonist prints will be submitted until an agreed show print is arrived at.

antagonist Person confronting the hero or protagonist, e.g. the baddie in the black hat versus the protagonist in the white hat.

Antares Name for a range of studio soft lights.

antenna American term for an aerial.

anti-flare An aerosol mixture used to spray on mirrors or bright surfaces to reduce flare from lights.

anti-halation backing Opaque backing to film stock which prevents reflections on to the emulsion from the plastic film base.

anti-hero Leading character who is at the same time sympathetic and either a victim of, or reject from, society, e.g. Chaplin's tramp or the main characters in the film *Bonnie & Clyde*. British soap operas and situation comedies extensively cultivate anti-heroes and anti- heroines. See **bathos**.

anti-reflection coating Transparent coating or bloom on a lens designed to cut out unwanted reflection.

anti-static An aerosol fluid sprayed on working surfaces and carpet to suppress static.

antiquing Artificially ageing a set or property. See **blowing down, breaking down**.

aperture The variable opening of a camera controlled by an iris mechanism which admits the light through the lens.

aperture correction Electronic means of correcting a loss of definition of fine detail in cameras.

aperture plate Metal plate on a camera or projector with a rectangular hole which defines the format of the film.

apostilb Metric unit used to measure light (luminance) from a surface.

applause light Lights around a studio in a light entertainment show bearing the word AP-PLAUSE which are flashed at appropriate moments to tell the invited audience when to burst into spontaneous hilarity despite the script. A production manager or floor manager may also clap his hands over his head animatedly to ram the point home for slow readers.

apple and biscuit An early type of omni- directional moving coil microphone, fancifully named because of its shape.

applebox A small rectangular rostrum.

appreciation index (AI) Means of graduating favourable or unfavourable audience response used by audience researchers.

approval print Alternative name for a film **answer print**.

Arab States Broadcasting Union (ASBU) The association of Arab-speaking broadcasting stations.

arc To pan a camera on a crane or jib.

arc lamp A powerful carbon-fed DC lamp.

archive film Film shot in the past, available from a film library.

Ariel BBC staff magazine, largely read for its job advertisements.

armourer Qualified person in charge of guns, explosives and edged weapons used as properties in a production.

Arriflex Trade name of **Arnold & Richter,** Munich. Particularly known for the range of lightweight 16mm film cameras which they pioneered. Often abbreviated to **Arri**.

art director A key figure in feature films responsible for every aspect of set decor, properties, costumes and set construction. The person who gives the visual 'feel' to a production by interpretation of the script.

art file A bolt-on device, which provides limited elements of Paintbox on a Rank Cintel slide file.

art movie 1. Film of an experimental or obscure nature appreciated by film buffs. 2. Dismissive term for a film of impressive self-indulgence, and sometimes as a euphemism for pornographic films.

artist Specifically someone working in design or graphics, but generally any creative contributor to a production.

artiste The terminal 'e' is an affectation which denotes an actor, extra or cabaret act performer. See **supporting artiste**.

Artists Index A list of performing artists with details of agents.

Asia-Pacific Institute for Broadcasting Development (AIBD) Association of Asian and Pacific States for training and programme exchange.

ashcan A single lighting unit with reflectors in a row of footlights.

aspect ratio The ratio of the width of a picture to its height. The normal TV aspect ratio is 4 x 3; cinema screens have a ratio of 5 x 4 (Academy Frame 1.33:1); HDTV systems are currently based on a 16 x 9 aspect ratio.

Aspheron An attachment which gives a standard lens an ultra-wide angle capacity.

assemble editing The simple butt-joining of picture, sound and control track on to a blank tape.

assembly The initial putting together of good takes from the sync rushes. This is the first stage of the creative editing process. Also known as a **rough cut**.

assembly/editing script A script provided by the director or production assistant which tells the film editor the sequence of shots to be assembled for the first cut of a programme.

assignments editor Editorial figure responsible for allocating crews and reporters to news stories.

assistant cameraman Cameraman's trainee

generally responsible for paperwork, checking equipment, loading magazines, putting on clapperboards and operating the camera under supervision.

assistant director (AD) Also called **first assistant**. Righthand person to the director on a feature film or commercial who is responsible for the organisation of a shoot and daily running of logistics and who may take charge of a second film unit. Second and third AD's approximate to roles of TV **assistant floor managers** or **floor assistants** in the BBC and **stage managers** in IBA companies. See **production manager**.

assistant film editor Operative responsible for syncing rushes, handling paperwork, arranging sound transfers and dubbing charts and generally helping in the cutting room.

assistant floor manager (AFM) A term mainly used in the BBC for the person with over- all responsibility for looking after artists, action props and day-to-day organisational problems on a shoot. Elsewhere known as **stage manager (SM)** or **assistant stage manager (ASM)**.

assistant sound recordist Assistant to the recordist who assists with the setting up of microphones and sound equipment and operating sound booms.

associate producer (AP) Righthand person to the producer. Sometimes in feature films the real executive, when the producer is the financial backer or a studio figurehead, sometimes a businessman or accountant rather than an artistic functionary.

Associated British Cinemas (ABC) One time main distributor of films in the UK.

Associated Press (AP) A press agency provid-

ing stories from a worldwide chain of news correspondents.

Associated Rediffusion One of the original
British commercial TV companies.

Association Française de Normalisation
(AFNOR) French body establishing technical
standards for film and television.

Association of Broadcasting Staff (ABS) One
of the two main British broadcasting trades union
formerly representing staff employed by the
BBC. Now absorbed into **BETA** .

**Association of Cinematograph and Televi-
sion Technicians(ACTT)** The trade union
dominant in the British feature film industry and
the ITV companies.

astigmatism A lens defect causing irregular
focusing and therefore blurring at the edges of a
frame. Lenses corrected for this fault are known
as **anastigmat.**

asynchronous sound Non-sync sound tracks
used in editing as a dramatic device. See **wild
track.**

atmos (atmosphere) General background
sound at a recording. An 'atmos' track is an important part of a sound recordist's duties. See
buzz track.

atmos mike A microphone placed away from
the main dialogue or action to record background
or ambient sounds simultaneously, e.g. an audience in a concert hall.

attenuator Device for reducing the volume of
an electronic signal without distortion.

audial filter (USA) See **sound filter.**

audible time code Time code can be recorded
on a special track or on a space audio track
where it can be heard as a staccato machine- gun-
like noise.

audience reaction Way in which audience researchers try to estimate the impact made upon a sample of viewers and expressed on a mathematical scale of 1 to 100.

audience research Public surveys in which viewing patterns are estimated by various sampling techniques. See **Broadcasting Audience Research Board**.

audio Sound or dialogue content of a production, as distinct from video, used to describe the picture content.

audio console Desk containing the controls for mixing the various sound inputs in a studio.

audio enhancement (USA) The manipulation of recorded sounds to achieve selected distortions, e.g. echo, delays, double tracking and so on. Much used to create pop records.

audio ring modulator Device where one signal can vary from another giving rise to a third signal, the process of modulation.

audio spectrum Range of sound frequencies to which a human ear responds.

audio sweetening (USA) The re-dubbing and modification of recorded sound on videotape. See **sypher**.

audio synthesiser Electronic generator which artificially creates musical effects.

audio-follow-video (USA) Facility for switching the acoustic of a soundtrack simultaneously with the vision cut.

audio-visual (A-V) Term used to describe multi-media presentations based upon projected slides and/or videotapes normally for live public display rather than broadcasting.

audition The selection of artists by asking them to perform pieces before the director or producer to help decide in casting roles.

auditorium The part of a concert hall or studio where the audience is seated. In some countries this may also mean a dubbing theatre.

Austin dolly Film dolly mounted on the chassis of an Austin car.

auteur French term for a film director who is in total control of the screenplay and content of a film rather than simply director of actors and cameras.

auto-focus System in which the camera is focused by means of an electronic sensing system. Of little use in serious cinematography where the selection of focal planes for artistic effect is one of the main arts of the cameraman.

auto-freeze Digital video track giving a strobe effect by freezing a continuous action.

autoblack (USA) Automatic adjustment of the black colour balance on a video camera.

Autocue A system for projecting the words of a script in front of a camera lens for a presenter to read in vision from a roller whose speed is controlled by an autocue operator.

automatic assembly editing A previously off-line compiled programme automatically re-edited by the computer editor.

automatic dialogue replacement (ADR) Sophisticated system of post-sync dubbing used in films where original filmed dialogue is recreated by actors after the film has been cut.

automatic gain control (AGC) A system whereby a recording machine automatically equalises the recorded volume of sounds. As a machine cannot distinguish between dialogue and the sound of a passing bus, the results are often the opposite of those intended by the manufacturers. Useful only to the amateur or when a news cameraman tries to record sound and pictures at the same time.

automatic iris A built-in lightmeter auto- matically controlling the exposure by regulating the iris of the lens.

automatic tracking The ability of a videotape recorder to adjust automatically the positions of its video replay head to produce maximum signal from tape.

autoscan tracking (AST) Manufacturer's name for automatic trailing adjustment of the tracking (head position) of videotape recorders. See **dynamic tracking (DT)**.

autowhite (USA) Video camera white balance control.

available light Light from naturally occurring sources such as windows or existing room lighting as opposed to controlled special artificial lighting on location.

avant garde Term originally used to describe experimental and innovative schools of French film makers but latterly often used to describe films which remain so individualistic as to be impenetrable to anyone but the director.

Avometer Brand of multimeter capable of measuring a range of voltages, currents and electrical resistances.

axial front projection (AFP) System for projecting images on a **lenticular screen** so that performers can appear to move around within projected image. The film camera has to remain at the same angle to the subject as the projector to achieve the illusion.

azimuth Geometrical alignment of the gap in tape replay or record head.

B AFTA See **British Academy of Film and Television Arts.**
BARB See **Broadcasting Audience Research Board.**

BBC British Broadcasting Corporation.

BBC Computer/Micro A small domestic computer marketed by the BBC.

BCC See **Broadcasting Complaints Commission.**

BCU Script abbreviation for **big close-up.**

BETA See **British Entertainment Trades Alliance.**

BFBS See **British Forces Broadcasting Services.**

BFI See **British Film Instititue.**

b/g Script abbreviation for **background.**

BKSTS See **British Kinematograph Sound and Television Society.**

BL See **blimped lightweight.**

BNC Type of plug and socket for video cables.

BP See **back projection.**

BT See **British Telecom** or **block termination.**

B/W Abbreviation for **black & white.**

B feature Cheap films billed as supporting features for main attractions at cinemas running double bills.

B side The flip side of a gramophone record.

B wind The commonest geometry for 16mm film. On single perforation 16mm film the sprocket holes face towards you when the film is wound clockwise and emulsion away from you.

babble Unintelligible signals on an audio track picked up from an unexpected source, e.g. taxi or police radio or a TV radio mike.

baby kicker A small light also called a **pup.**

baby legs A small tripod used to achieve steady low-angle shots.

baby spot Stage and TV term for a tiny spotlight, normally of 100 or 150 watts, used to highlight details on a set.

back cue To cue up and run a disc or tape prior to its actual transmission enabling it to be faded up at a determined point.

back focus The adjustment of a zoom lens to ensure that the image produced is sharply focused upon the image plane throughout the zoom range. (Normally an engineering adjustment).

back light A light used to illuminate the action from behind to increase the sense of depth from the background. One of the three main luminaires used for simple TV lighting, the others being the **keylight** and the **filler**.

back pack A frame worn on the back of an electronic portable camera operator or his assistant for carrying batteries, recording equipment or transmitter. Now largely obsolete.

back porch The part of the television waveform before the end of an active television line and the start of a sync pulse.

back projection (BP) Background images projected from behind on a translucent screen with the actors performing in front.

back timing Technique used by production assistants to work back from a given point within or at the end of a programme in order to meet that exact time.

back, knife in Simple tactic whereby one television employee gains precedence over another.

back, smile in Urbane BBC alternative to above.

backcloth/backdrop Cloth backing to a studio set or stage which is frequently painted with a scene.

background atmosphere Part of a composite

recorded sound track consisting of a constant general effect, e.g. traffic noise, surf, birdsong.

background music Specially supplied musical accompaniment to a scene used to enhance dramatic impact as opposed to **source music**.

background plate Still picture used in back projection.

backgrounder Newsroom term for researched item attempting to explain, rather than simply describe, topical events.

backing 1. Scenery to be seen on a set through an open window or door. 2. Carbon coating on the reverse of colour film.

backing track A sound track, usually instrumental, recorded by a musical group to which solos, vocals, etc can be added in performance or final recording.

backlaying Film editing technique in which the film is synchronised from the end rather than the start of a shot, usually because of an end board.

backstage Any area behind a theatre stage or television set, generally referring to dressing rooms, make-up areas, wardrobes, etc, regardless of the exact geographical location.

backup schedule Known familiarly as 'Plan B'. A list of alternative shoots which may be needed due to possible changes of weather, e.g. last minute swapping of exterior and interior scenes.

baffle 1. A sound-absorbent screen used to deaden echo or isolate performers in a sound recording. 2. Louvred shutter on the front of a studio lamp.

balance 1. (audio) The relative adjustment of the volume or level of audio sources to achieve the correct dramatic relationship between them.

2. (lighting) Regulation of the intensity of a group of lights normally using flesh tones as a point of reference both to achieve an aesthetically satisfying picture and ensure that the contrast of light and dark are within the technical range of the cameras being used. **3.** (picture composition) The moving of props, scenery or the positioning of actors to give a more pleasing symmetry to the composition of a shot.

balanced pair Audio line where the circuit conductors are electrically symmetrical, making it less susceptible to interference pickup.

balancing stripe On commag film, a narrow strip of magnetic tape is often placed on the opposite side of the film carrying the recording stripe to equalize the thickness of the stock when winding the roll.

banana plug Type of electric monopole plug which, to the engineering eye looks a bit like a banana.

banana skin See **bathos**.

band 1. Group of musical performers. **2.** Abbreviation for waveband or bandwidth. **3.** A particular track on a record.

banding Fault on a segmented format VTR (e.g. 2-inch Quad) where the picture appears to break up into a series of horizontal bands.

bandwidth A span of frequencies needed to achieve a sound or picture signal.

bank On a vision mixing panel a discrete set of buttons, e.g. A Bank, B Bank, Preview Bank, etc. Called a **bus** in the USA.

bank overlay Standard chromakey facility operated from a studio gallery by a vision mixer.

Baptys London supplier of firearms and edged weapons for dramatic use.

bar 1. A division in a musical score used

specifically in television to count the timing of cuts in musical items. **2.** The place where important decisions are made in most TV companies.

bar chart Graphic illustration of statistics in the form of horizontal bars.

bar counting Job of a production assistant, which involves breaking down a musical score into its composite bars and calling them out by number in the gallery for the guidance of the director and vision mixer.

Barco A manufacturer of video projection systems and monitors.

barn doors Hinged metal flaps fitted in front of lamps to adjust the spill of light.

barney Cameraman's term for a flexible cloth blimp placed over a camera to suppress motor noise.

barrel A hanging bar for suspending studio lights.

barrel distortion Fault in a lens or camera tube giving rise to a compression of the corners of the image making the normally square frame seem barrel shaped.

barracuda Telescopic metal pole for lights.

barron box A stagemanager's or commentator's communication box at an outside event.

bars/colour bars An electronic test signal consisting of vertical saturated colour stripes used to adjust vision equipment for its optimum performance.

bars (USA) See **barrel**.

base **1.** The physical fabric of the film on which the light-sensitive emulsion is laid; nowadays of cellulose acetate or polyester, but formerly of nitrate. **2.** Make-up term for the general skin tone cosmetic upon which subsequent details are created.

base light General background light or filler.

baseplate A metal plate fitted to the base of a camera which allows it to be attached to the head of a tripod or other camera mounting.

basher/hand-basher 1. A location portable battery light. Also known as **sun gun**.
2. Portable floor light on a stand mainly used to improve portraiture.

bass Bottom end of a musical scale.

bassy Opposite of **toppy**. Sound in which the lower register is noticeably emphasized or the treble is reduced.

batch number Serial numbers printed by a manufacturer on packs of videotape or film to indicate that their coating or emulsion was prepared at the same time and therefore there should be no variation in technical performance, film speed or colour sensitivity.

bath General term to describe the film processing laboratories; specifically the tank containing the chemicals.

bathos Dramatic comic technique of allowing a scene to develop from the sublime to the ridiculous, or to defuse a dramatic build-up with a foolish or comic resolution, e.g. the classic pompous-man-slipping-on-the-banana-skin joke.

battery belt A belt carrying the battery for some portable electronic cameras worn by the camera operator or assistant. Also regularly worn by an electrician whilst operating a sun gun.

battery light A **basher** or **sun gun**. A portable location lamp.

bazooka An adjustable monopod which can take a short jib arm and is used in restricted locations where a dolly or tripod would take up too much space.

beaded screen Highly reflective screen

particularly used for front axial projection.

beam 1. Focused light. 2. Stream of electrons in a cathode-ray tube emitted from an electron gun.

beam focus Adjustment of an electron beam in relation to its target.

beanstalk Portable scaffolding which can be assembled from interlocking sections to reach studio lanterns, etc.

bearding See **tearing**.

beat Rhythmic sub-division of a bar of music used by production assistants and vision mixers to judge picture cuts in musical item.

Beaulieu French make of film equipment.

beep/beeper 1. Audio signal identifying the beginning of a recording. 2. Means of wiping out random obscenities. See **bleep**.

Bell & Howell A manufacturer of film equipment.

Bell & Howell mechanism Intermittent camera shutter mechanism developed in the 1930's.

Bell & Howell perforation Sprocket holes with slightly curved sides.

bellows Extending fabric fitment to front of camera to exclude flare from the lens.

below the line Description of production costs which may be considered part of the available resources of a production company, e.g. staff salaries, own film equipment, office accommodation, etc. See **above the line**.

benchwork Synonym for rostrum camera work, in which still pictures or photographs are attached to a moving bench beneath a camera mounted overhead. Used particularly to give animation to still pictures or to film captions.

bend the needle Recordist's term for wildly

excessive sound which causes the needle on the volume meter to go off the end of the register on the dial.

Bermans & Nathans London suppliers of wardrobe costumes for theatrical, film and television productions.

best boy Chief gofer on a film studio stage. Frequently subdivided into best boy (lights) and best boy (grips).

Betacam Half-inch tape format developed by Sony.

Betacassette Videotape half-inch cassette system used by the Betacam.

bi-directional microphone Microphone which picks up sound both in front and behind, therefore suitable for radio studio interviews, etc.

bias light A means of minimising low-light lag in television camera tubes.

bicycle To pass programmes on from station to station or country to country in sequence for successive rentals and transmission.

big close-up Abbreviated to BCU on scripts. A very large shot showing a close detail of an object or of a human face from chin to hairline. Sometimes called **extremely close-up (ECU)**.

big ears Type of photographic slide projector with two banks of slides mounted in round magazines like Mickey Mouse ears.

Big Five The main five British commercial TV companies whose 'club' produces and networks the overwhelming majority of commercial television programmes (Central, Granada, London Weekend, Thames and Yorkshire TV).

biggie A really sensational story for which every journalist lives in hope.

billings 1. Relative position and size of print in the list of credits at the end of a film, often the cause of much bickering and histrionics amongst actors and their agents. **2.** Printed details of a programme detailing cast and transmission times. **3.** Value of accounts handled by an advertising agency.

bin Container for film trims and loose film during the editing process. Also sometimes the waste bin into which rejected film is dumped.

binaural recording Stereo sound recording system with microphones placed in the 'ears' of a dummy human head. Only really works when replayed via headphones.

bio-pic Hollywood term for the filmed biography of an historical personage.

bipack film Two films of different characteristics run through a printer simultaneously for special effects, e.g. **travelling mattes**.

bird A satellite.

birding (USA) Transmitting material by communications satellite; so called because of an early satellite known as 'Early Bird'.

bit part A small acting part in a film, usually involving some dialogue.

biz (USA) Abbreviation for business.

bizphone (USA) A direct exchange telephone line.

black & white (B/W) Layman's term for monochrome film or TV. In reality, a picture displayed in shades of grey.

black clipper Electronic control that ensures that the picture content does not go below black level.

black comedy Film or programme which takes tragic or revolting subject matter and treats it in an absurd or humorous way with satirical intent.

black crushing Compression of darker parts

of a picture area leading to a loss of significant detail.

black edging An electronic means of making white lettering more prominent when superimposed on a picture by outlining it in black.

black level Electronic reference point, representing 'true' black. See **peak white**.

black light Mainly a theatrical term to describe the use of ultra-violet or infra-red light to achieve special effects.

black limbo (USA) Completely black cyclorama and stage floor in which lit performers appear to be suspended. See **infinity cyclorama**.

black-and-burst A television signal containing all the necessary synchronising information for a colour picture but where the picture content is black. Videotapes are prepared for insert editing by recording continuous black-and-burst.

blackout Total extinction of lights, normally at the end of a programme or for a dramatic effect.

blacks 1. Black velvet curtains frequently used in place of an illuminated cyclorama, particularly in studio settings. 2. The dark part of a scene.

blanking 1. Opaque film used as spacing in film editing and track laying. 2. The area between active television lines or fields where the synchronising information is carried.

blast filter (USA) A microphone wind **gag**.

bleach bath Part of the film development process in which the exposed silver image is chemically revealed prior to immersion in the fixing solution.

bleep Electronic sound used to obliterate undesirable or obscene words. Usually draws attention to the problem.

bleep tone System for automatically boarding film whereby a frame of film is flashed and a noise is put upon the sound track when the camera turns over.

bleeper Portable receiver used in an electronic paging system.

blimp A soundproof housing for a camera. Most television cameras are self-blimped, i.e. the bodywork and magazines are designed to absorb most motor noise except in close-up work when a **barney** is used.

blimped lightweight (BL) 16mm film camera manufactured by Arnold & Richter: for a long period the standard sound television film camera.

blind bidding Distributors' habit of bargaining for exhibition or transmission rights to films or programmes before actually viewing them.

blind wipe Electronic effect achieving a wipe from one scene to another whilst looking like the action of venetian window blinds.

block booking 1. A commercial practice in which film and television companies purchase a number of inferior products in order to buy rights to prestigious films from the same source. **2.** A practice whereby one production office will book a facility throughout the run of a series, in anticipation of its use, thus rendering it unavailable to anyone else who might need it!

block termination All necessary communications circuits installed by British Telecom for an outside broadcast.

blockbuster A wildly successful production (usually also a wildly expensive one).

blocking Rehearsal stage in which artists' moves are broken down and finalised with a view to the placing of cameras, lights and microphones. In studio, this is the initial camera rehearsal period where artist and camera moves are rehearsed individually prior to running the complete sequence.

blocks Solid boxes of various sizes used on stage or in studio to support or raise furniture, props and short cameramen.

blonde A 2 kW light used in portable TV film lighting kits. So named because a leading manufacturer enamels them yellow. See **redheads**.

blood chit 1. Term for an instant contract issued to a member of the public on location for all rights to use their picture or words in a transmitted programme. **2.** A form of indemnity or waiver of insurance insisted upon, particularly by the armed forces, before staff or artists can travel in any of their vehicles, aircraft or equipment.

BLOOD CHIT

bloomed lens. See **coated lens**.

blooming 1. Process of coating a lens to reduce the amount of reflection from the optics and increase the amount of light which passes to the film. 2. Electronic picture fault. See **puddling**.

blooping ink Ink used by editors working on optical film sound to blot out undesirable noises on the track, particularly at the points where the film has been cut.

blow 1. To ruin completely, as in '*the actor blew his entrance/script*', i.e. he wrecked his cue/lines. 2. A fuse, bulb or electrical connection suddenly failing.

blow down Spraying the surface of a set or prop with paint or lacquer to dampen its brightness or intensity of colour, or to impart the patina of age.

blow-up Enlarged photograph incorporated as part of a set. Frequently called photo blow up (PBU).

blueing A technique for balancing interior and exterior light. A cameraman may compensate for the difference between colour temperatures by putting blue gels over light sources.

board 1. The clapperboard used at the beginning or end of every film take. 2. Alternative term for takes, e.g.'*we shot 24 boards on Friday*'.

board it! Instruction by a director or camera operator to mark a scene with the clapper. Also '*mark it!*'.

boat truck A low platform on castors for moving scenery or, when sprung, to simulate the movement of a car or train.

Bolex 16mm cameras mainly used for mute filming and amateur work.

booker Company employee concerned with

negotiating contracts with performing artists.

boom A manœuvrable and extendable arm used to suspend microphones over the actor but out of camera shot. Handled by a boom operator.

boom dolly The wheeled unit on which the counterweighted microphone boom arm is mounted.

boom down! Gallery director's instruction for microphones to be lowered nearer to the action.

boom mike Microphone mounted on a swivel and suspended from an extending boom which can be swung in any direction and is used for most studio sound, particularly in drama.

boom shadow A shadow accidentally thrown upon a set or action due to the boom microphone being caught in front of the key light.

boom swinger Studio operator of a microphone boom.

boom up! Gallery director's instruction for microphone to be removed from shot.

boomy Distortion in a room where reverberation of low frequencies gives a deep, echo-like acoustic. Also known as **boxy**.

Boosey & Hawkes Music publishers specialising in recorded background music discs and tapes.

booster A particularly strong developing solution added to processing chemicals.

booster station A transmitter used to relay programmes to areas that have difficulty in receiving the main transmitter's output.

booth Soundproof enclosure used for the camera in projection theatres or for the commentator in film dubbing suites.

booth porthole Window in projection theatre allowing the projector beam to fall on to the screen.

border generator An electronic device or a vision mixing/editing desk for generating coloured edges on wipes.

Border Television Commercial television company with the franchise for Cumbria and the Scottish Borders.

bottle Cameraman's slang for a **lens**.

bought-in programme Commercial which is purchased from an outside production company.

bounce To point lamps at reflective surfaces, e.g. white ceilings, so as to reflect light rather than shine the light source directly upon the subject.

box 1. Acoustically-tested booth in a dubbing theatre where a commentator sits to record the commentary to picture. **2.** On sports OBs, the booth for the commentator.

box office Originally the booth in a theatre where tickets are sold, but now generally used to describe the gross receipts of a film, e.g. a film may be described as good or bad box office.

box out/box down To close down the barn door shutters on a lamp to restrict the beam to a narrow spot.

box set A highly naturalistic theatrical studio set, involving a three or four-wall construction, which restricts cameras, sound booms and lighting.

boxy A resonant acoustic common in unfurnished rooms. See **boomy**.

brace Adjustable support for a stage flat, anchored by a hook at one end and a stage weight at the other.

brace iron The projecting metal foot of a stage brace.

bracketing Photographic technique. When an exposure is critical, the scene is shot first at the exposure indicated by the exposure meter and then at one stop over and one stop under to give optimum choice for the final print.

brail Theatre or studio term to describe the securing of any hanging prop or piece of scenery.

break 1. A story breaks when it ceases to be hearsay or private knowledge and becomes, or can be made, public. **2.** A planned interval in transmission to accommodate TV or radio commercials.

break down To simulate wear and tear on fresh theatrical costumes by applying dust, dirt and creases.

breakaway 1. An action property or part of a set designed to look solid but to break easily without harm to a performer. **2.** (USA) A simple animation using a card caption. A **reveal**.

breakdown 1. Equipment failure, sometimes applied to similar symptoms amongst personnel. **2.** The act of dismantling a studio set. **3.** The reduction of a script into sequences for filming or recording schedules.

breakdown script (USA) A shooting schedule.

breaker 1. A switch controlling the electrical power to a technical area. See also **trip switch**. **2.** Device to protect against fire hazard in an electrical installation by interrupting the power in the event of an overload. See **MCB** and **earth leakage circuit breaker**.

Breakfast TV Live topical magazine programme broadcast continuously from the early hours of the morning until around 9 a.m.

breaking down The process of taking sound and picture film rushes and splitting up the rolls into the individual slates after they have been put in sync. These are then hung up in the trim bin in numbered order for the film editor to select.

breakthrough Unwanted sound from one recorded track or source.

breakthrough piece Film scenery which can be moved during a shot to enable a tracking camera to pass.

breathe on To take an apparently indifferent story and give it an appearance of significance or entertainment value by clever production or direction technique.

breathing 1. A fault on a camera lens or projector on which there is a fluctuation in focus, caused by a fluttering of the film in a camera or projector gate or by spontaneous movements on a zoom lens. **2.** Audible changes in background sound as the recording level is adjusted to cope with variations in foreground sound, especially associated with automatic compressors.

bridge/bridging shot Picture or musical sequence which covers a transition between two very different scenes or programme items.

brief 1. Outline of a story given by a researcher to a reporter or director or by a director to the crew. **2.** In criminal parlance, a barrister or solicitor.

briefing Public statements given to journalists at a press conference.

brightness 1. The amount of illumination overall on a TV screen. **2.** Name of the control for the black level on a TV set.

brilliance 1. Brightness. **2.** Term used to describe the sharpness and clarity of a sound recording.

British Academy of Film and Television Arts (BAFTA) A club for those in the film and television industries whose annual awards are the closest the British come to an Oscar ceremony.

British Actors' Equity The main trade union

for actors, usually known simply as **Equity**.

British Board of Film Classification Successor to British Board of Film Censors. Body responsible for classifying films for public theatrical performances according to their supposed suitability for different age groups.

British Entertainment Trade Alliance (BETA) The leading British film and television trade union.

British Film Institute(BFI) Body formed to encourage the study of film as an artform. Incorporates the National Film Archives and the National Film Theatre as well as supporting regional theatres. Publishes *Sight & Sound*, the magazine for British film buffs.

British Forces Broadcasting Services (BFBS) Radio and television service for British armed forces garrison overseas. Amalgamated with the Services Kinematograph Corporation into the SSVC (Services Sound & Vision Corporation).

British Kinematograph Sound and Television Society (BKSTS). Society for encouraging the technical and scientific development of film and television.

British Library National Sound Archive. See **National Sound Archive**.

British Telecom (BT) Main British telephone and telecommunication company. Generally abbreviated to **Telecom**.

broad A soft unfocused lamp used for back or filler lighting.

broadcast quality Engineers' term to describe the technical specifications of equipment for professional broadcasters to distinguish them from those of industrial or semi-professional equipment deemed fit only for closed-circuit work. A source of constant controversy between engineers and programme makers.

broadcasting The transmission of sound or pictures intended for general public reception, opposite of **closed circuit television, cable TV** or **narrowcasting**.

Broadcasting Audience Research Board (BARB) Agency for compiling viewing figures and audience reactions covering both the BBC and ITV companies

Broadcasting Complaints Commission (BCC) A statutory body set up to deal with complaints of unfit or unjust treatment or unwarranted infringement of privacy by broadcasting companies.

brother-in-law Contemptuous early Hollywood term for a film director suggesting his relationship to the producer as his main qualification for the job.

brute A large carbon arc lamp of 225 amps fitted with a Fresnel lens.

bubble Electricians' slang for a **lamp bulb.**

bubble machine Apparatus for generating bubbles, e.g. in a bathroom sequence.

bubble memory Electronic memory system for data storage.

bubble time Electricians' rhyming slang for overtime brought about by a location or studio overrun, i.e. bubble = double time; double bubble = double the usual hourly rate.

buddy film Film in which two male companions support each other in their adventures. A genre of 60's and 70's feature films, e.g. *Butch Cassidy and the Sundance Kid.*. A much used formula in later TV series, e.g. *Starsky and Hutch,* or its female equivalent *Cagney and Lacey.*

budget Amount of money allocated to a programme; **low budget show** A cheap show which the producer complains is starved of funds; **big budget show** A wildly expensive show where the producer makes the same complaint.

buff See **film buff**.

buffer shot A shot inserted into an edited sequence to carry one sequence to another or to avoid an unhappy jump in action or continuity.

bug 1. An unidentifiable or untraceable fault in a piece of engineering equipment blamed by engineers on manufacturers, operators and divine intervention. 2. A concealed microphone. See **gremlin, Murphy's law, sod's law**.

bugging The practice of concealing microphones or recording equipment to catch a scene unawares: subject to stringent regulations by TV companies and involving legal restrictions.

build To heighten dramatic impact through increasing tension progressively in the action or the editing.

build-up 1. Technique for recording and re-recording videotape for a special effect, e.g. having the same actor appearing two or more times in the same picture in much the same way as a double exposure in stills photography. 2. Accumulated scrapings of emulsion in a film gate. Commonest source of a **hair in the gate**. 3. Sections of blank spacer film used to replace missing bits of picture or sound in the editing or film track-laying process. 4. The orchestrated publicising of an artist or programme prior to transmission. See **hype**.

bulb Cameraman's slang for the bowl-shaped base of a fluid head camera mount.

bulk eraser Machine for wiping clean magnetic sound or videotapes for re-use by demagnetizing them.

bull horn (USA) See **loudhailer**.

bulletin A news programme appearing at regular times.

bungie An electric plug.

Burbank Suburb of Los Angeles which is home to many film and television studios.

burn The result of pointing an electronic camera at a brilliant light source, with the result that the camera tubes are temporarily or permanently damaged and retain the image as a superimposition over subsequent shots.

burn out The result of over-exposure or when an electronic camera or film emulsion cannot cope with extremes of contrast. The result is that white or light parts of a picture appear as blank areas destroying all detail or tones.

burn through (USA) Over-exposed captions superimposed over an image.

bus (USA) A bank of buttons.

Bush House Headquarters of the BBC **World Service** situated in the Aldwych, Central London.

business Any minor movement or bit of action devised by an actor or director to enhance the performance or direction.

business theatre Pretentious description for multi-media events which mix closed circuit video and/or tape slide with live action on a stage.

busk it/wing it. Expression that denotes the need to improvise because of lack of time or planning.

bust shot (USA) A mid-close up shot showing head and shoulders.

busy Description of a set or scene in which too many elements of design tend to give a cluttered or confused impression.

butt join Two sequences of film or videotape joined with neither sound nor picture overlapping.

button puncher The studio director; a term often used by news journalists who know no better.

buzz A real thrill.

buzz track A continuous sound track taken by a recordist on location of local atmosphere. It enables the film editor or dubbing mixer to cover jumps in sound level and acoustic in an edited sequence and to cover mute shots which have to be cut into a sequence of shots.

buzzer cue Means of communicating between distant technical facilities by means of a buzzer. Usually videotape and telecine operators are remote from the studio gallery and communicate by buzzer such as: one buzz = yes, two buzzes = no.

C **ATV** See **Community Antenna Television**.

CCD See **charge coupled device**.

CCIR See *Comité Consultative International des Radiocommunications*.

CCTV See **closed circuit television**.

CCU See **camera control unit**.

CD See **compact disc**.

CDS See **cadmium disulphide**.

CID See **compact iodine discharge**.

CMCCR See **combined mobile central control room**.

CMCR See **colour mobile control room**.

CNN See **Cable News Network**.

COI See **Central Office of Information**.

cps See **cycles per second**.

CPU See **caption projection unit**.

CRT See **cathode ray tube**.

CSO See **colour separation overlay**.

CU Script abbreviation for **close-up**.

C mount A screw lens mounting commonly used on 16mm film cameras.

Cable News Network (CNN) American nationwide twenty-four hour news service available to cable subscribers.

cable release Remote control mechanism for operating a camera shutter.

cable run A connected length of cable between camera, sound or lighting points.

cable TV TV which is distributed to households from a common aerial through cables. Specifically commercial companies which redistribute broadcast programmes or their own programmes through cables.

cable-basher Junior member of a studio crew whose job is to pay out camera cables. Essential in the days when studio camera cables were heavy and inflexible.

cableman (USA) A cable-basher.

Cabot's quilt Duvet-like, temporary sound proofing.

cadmium disulphide (CDS) The chemical compound used in light-sensitive cells, e.g. exposure meters.

Cahiers du Cinema Influential French magazine originally founded in 1947 and devoted to film criticism. A bible for film buffs.

cake See **pancake**.

calibration Marking on a lens which shows the aperture and focus.

call (USA) Station or channel identification signal or announcement.

call boy Employee responsible for calling artists from the dressing and make-up rooms and getting them to the set or location on cue. Due to women's liberation and consequent ambiguity in its feminine form, the term now used is generally **floor/stage assistant**.

call sheet Daily schedule of appearance times for artists during rehearsal or recordings.

call time The summons to performers to assemble at a given time and place in preparation for a shoot. See **rendezvous**.

cam 1. Abbreviation for **camera**. 2. Revolving device within a camera activating the claws which pull the film through the mechanism.

cam remote (USA) A hot head camera mounting. See **hot head**.

camcorder (USA) An electronic camera in which the recorder is an integral part of the camera housing, e.g. **Betacam**.

cameo Brief guest appearance by a star performer in a minor scene. A device used on long-running or jaded TV soap operas.

cameo lighting (USA) Black limbo lighting. See **limbo shot**.

camera angles The range of possible positions which a camera can take in relation to a subject, e.g. **high angle**, **low angle**, **wide angle**, etc.

camera blocking See **blocking** .

camera cable Multi-cored cable connecting an electronic camera either to its camera control unit or to a video recorder.

camera card/crib card A card listing and describing in sequence the particular shots assigned to one of several cameras in a multi-camera electronic studio.

camera chain Collectively, the various items of equipment which together enable a television image to be made. They include the camera, the camera control unit, the control panel and the power supply unit. Used to describe the equipment collectively in electronic studios.

camera channel Description of a complete working set of camera equipment, including tripod, sound recorder, microphones etc, but excluding lights.

camera control operator Operator of remote controls for video cameras in the electronic studio.

camera control unit (CCU) Electronic controls for a video camera. Normally installed in a control room or engineering area.

camera cue light Lamp on top of a studio camera indicating that it is live and on air. Traditionally red.

camera head The mechanical device between the body of a camera and its dolly or tripod which enables it to pan and tilt.

camera jam Nightmare of film cameramen and directors in which a failure of the mechanism or bad lacing causes the film to jump off its sprockets and pile up inside the camera.

camera lamp A light mounted on the front of a camera. Also called a **headlamp**.

camera left/right Left and right as perceived by a camera looking towards a scene or performance. The reverse of **stage left** and **right**.

camera matching The balancing of exposure, black level and colour rendition of studio cameras so that they produce matching pictures.

camera mounting Tripods, dollies, cranes, etc, on which a camera can be positioned.

camera movements Various ways in which a camera physically alters its position, e.g. **pan** or **tilt** from a static position, or **track** or **crab** when mounted as a wheeled **dolly** on tracks.

camera obscura (*Latin* = dark room). Device invented by Leonardo da Vinci who observed that a pinpoint of light admitted to a darkened room and falling on a screen produced an exact inverted image of the exterior scene — thereby origin of the term 'camera' to describe all subsequent photographic devices.

camera operator In cases where the chief cameraman is concerned exclusively with lighting and setting a scene, a second cameraman or assistant may be used to operate the camera equipment. Always so in Hollywood but less common with U.K. crews.

camera original The film, either negative or reversal, on which the exposure is made.

camera point Fixed point on a studio wall from which electronic cameras can be cabled.

camera rehearsal Rehearsal in the studio, on stage or location for the benefit of the lighting cameraman to establish or confirm camera moves, angles, etc.

camera script Programme script marked up with shot numbers, camera positions and cues.

camera tape Adhesive cloth tape used for sealing film cans, magazines, etc, and a hundred other small location jobs.

camera tower A scaffolding tower constructed for an outside broadcast camera.

camera trap Part of a set constructed to conceal a camera which otherwise might appear in vision. See **trap**.

camera tube One device which converts light energy into an electrical signal. An evacuated glass envelope houses a light sensitive target on which the image is focused, and an electron gun from which a focused beam of electrons scans the target, reading out the point-by-point image intensity.

camera van Vehicle used for storage and transportation of outside broadcast camera and sound equipment, monitors and stands.

cameraman **1.** Male or female operator of a film or electronic camera who is part of a studio or outside broadcast crew. **2.** The director of photography in a film crew and the senior technician also in charge overall of lights and sound.

camp To overplay a part in an obviously stagey and affected way.

camping Exaggerated and sexually ambivalent behaviour.

can The metal container in which a film is kept.

candid camera Film method in which unsuspecting members of the public are caught in a real situation or a contrived set-up and filmed without their knowledge, frequently for comic effect.

candles/foot candles/candela A scale for measuring the intensity of light.

canned drama (USA) Contemptuous early term for cinema feature films, distinguishing them from live theatrical performances.

canned laughter/applause Recorded enthusiasm from an invisible audience, dubbed on to a recorded programme, to give an impression of uncontrollable hilarity where actual reactions might appear to be less than flattering to the production.

canned music Pre-recorded musical sound track. See **muzak**.

cannon connector Torpedo-shaped male/female plug.

Canon Japanese manufacturer of camera lenses and photographic equipment.

cans Synonym for earphones or headphones.

canted shot **1.** Dramatic shot in which the camera is deliberately placed at an unnatural angle to the horizon. Much used in pop music videos and as a means of heightening tension and a sense of unreality in some kinds of direction, e.g. Carol Reed's *The Third Man*. Also called **Dutch angle**. **2.** (USA) A shot taken from an extreme high or low angle.

canvas drop A painted **backcloth**.

cap **1.** To cover the front of a lens either physically with a lens cap or by an electronic control. **2.** Abbreviation of **caption**.

capacitor microphone See **condenser microphone**.

caption A card carrying graphics or words, also used to describe any kind of electronically-generated typographic artwork in a programme.

caption card Cardboard used for mounting letters, numbers or artwork. Usually used in television format sizes, e.g. 12 x 9 or 20 x 15 inches.

caption generator Mechanism for electronically typing names, titles, etc, on to the television screen.

caption light Stand light on the studio floor used for illuminating card captions.

caption projection unit (CPU) Metal box unit with a screen at one end and slide projection at the other, allowing a studio camera to pan or zoom over a projected picture.

caption puller Studio operative whose job is to change captions in front of a camera at the director's instruction.

caption roller Mechanical device for running continuous graphic material in front of a camera, e.g. closing credits.

caption scanner **1.** A small fixed monochrome camera used to feed 12 x 9-inch captions on card into a studio programme. **2.** Device for producing TV pictures from 35mm slides.

caption stand Stand for mounting cardboard captions on a studio floor.

captive audience Audience invited to attend a recording or transmission, who effectively become participants in the programme.

car park job Emergency procedure for picking up a shot or scene neglected on location, which is shot in the nearest available free space and subsequently cut in to the main action in the hope that nobody will notice.

carbon arc High intensity lamp in which a direct current passes between two carbon electrodes and which emits a colour temperature very similar to daylight.

cardioid mike A microphone whose effective field for picking up sound is heart-shaped.

careen shot (USA) A shot which is transmitted back to base from an outside broadcast by bouncing it off a dish placed on a tall building.

carnet Customs import/export document itemising precise details of equipment needed by location crews travelling abroad to avoid risk of confiscation or arrest.

carousel A still slide projector or pair of projectors loaded with circular magazines, often remotely controlled from the gallery. See **caption projection unit (CPU)**.

carrier wave/carrier signal The high-frequency signal carrying sound and video between transmitter and receiver.

cart Abbreviation for **sound cartridge**.

cart play! (USA) News gallery instruction to run videotape from a U-matic cartridge.

cartoon An animated film produced entirely from artwork.

cartridge 1. Cassettes loaded with quarter-inch tape used particularly in radio for playing in recorded commercials and musical stings.
2. (USA) A video cassette.

cascadeur French term for a stuntman.

cassette Self-contained box containing sound or videotape as distinct from reel-to-reel tape playing.

cassette machine Machine for playing sound and/or video cassettes.

cast list List of performers in a drama.

casting Selecting of performers for appropriate roles, normally after audition. Also selection of suitable directors, etc, by a producer.

casting couch Legendary furniture essential to directors supposedly used in the auditioning of actresses and actors.

casting director Studio executive in feature

film studios responsible for the selection and contracting of performers.

cat head A swinging arm fixed to the top of a camera scaffold tower, used to attach lifting hoist.

catchlight (USA) Light reflection from the eyes of a performer in a close-up shot.

cathode ray tube (CRT) Generic term for the display tube on television sets/oscilloscopes or radar screens.

catwalk Suspended overhead walkway in a studio giving access to lighting equipment.

Ceefax The BBC's video news and information service available on domestic receivers. See **teletext** .

cel Transparent sheet of cellulose acetate used for artwork in film animations.

celebrity Someone who appears regularly on TV because he/she is famous for appearing on TV. See **personality**, **star**, **compere**.

celluloid Cellulose derived base for film stocks, filters, artwork transparencies, etc. Widely, but inaccurately, used term for any transparent material. See **nitrate film stock**.

cement Adhesive used to join film, now almost only used in negative cutting.

censor key (USA) See **bleep**.

censor title Title in advance of a programme indicating that the transmission has been passed for exhibition to defined categories of audience by an official body.

Central (Central Independent Television) Commercial television company holding the franchise for the English Midland counties.

central apparatus room An area set aside for housing much of the technical equipment associated with the distribution and routeing of signals around a station, or to and from outside destinations.

Central Office of Information (COI)   British government agency responsible for public service films and broadcasts as well as documentary films sponsored by British and Commonwealth government departments.

centre stage The middle of a scene or set.

centre up! Director's instruction to a studio camera operator to correct the composition by placing the main subject centre of frame.

century stand (USA) Tripod stand used to support diffusers, vignettes, etc in front of lamps or cameras.

chain See **camera chain**.

changeover Point in projection or **telecine** where one reel ends and another begins and the operator switches from one machine to another.

changeover cue Perforated spots at the end of one film roll instructing a projectionist to change over to a subsequent roll on a second machine. See **cue dot**.

changing bag A lightproof black bag used on location by the assistant film cameraman for reloading magazines.

channel **1.** A frequency allocated to a TV or radio service. **2.** A complete set of film equipment including camera, camera mountings and sound equipment (UK).

Channel 4 British commercial TV channel which commissions work from independent companies rather than producing programmes of its own.

Channel 4 (Wales) See **Sianel Pedwar Cymru**.

Channel Television Commercial television company serving the British Channel Islands.

channel zapping/hopping Habit of using a domestic remote control to skip rapidly between broadcast channels to avoid commercial breaks or to keep up with more than one programme at a time.

chaperone An adult guardian legally required to accompany child performers.

Chappell Music Music publishers specialising in recorded background music.

character actor Performer who specialises in one distinctive type of role.

character generator Electronic equipment for directly superimposing word graphics, name captions, etc, over a programme.

character make-up Make-up intended to disguise or alter the normal appearance of a performer rather than to flatter or enhance natural looks.

characteristic curve The way the exposure of a television camera or film stock varies with different colours.

charge coupled device (CCD) A silicon chip with a light-sensitive layer used as an alternative to a camera tube in video cameras. See **chip camera.**

charger Device for putting an electrical charge into a battery.

Charlie Bar A narrow French flag.

Charisma A type of video electronic effects generator.

chart A board marked with a grid pattern placed in front of cameras for registration and line-up.

charts Popularity tables for pop music compiled from weekly record sales.

chat show A discussion programme usually occupying itself with life's trivialities, the cheapest form of television. See **personality, celebrity, star**.

cheapo/cheapie A programme made on the smallest possible budget to fill up the available airtime without too much attention to quality. See **chat show**.

cheat eyeline A way of improving a performer's position in relation to other actors or to the camera which breaks continuity, but which succeeds in deceiving the viewer.

cheat shot A shot in an intercut sequence which is arranged for better composition or to disguise a clumsy move which strictly is illogical but in fact will look convincing to the audience.

checkerboard For A and B roll editing or printing in which sequences are alternated with blank spacing on two rolls to enable telecine to mix between the two.

cheek Circular disc on a film winding bench.

chemical mixer Film laboratory technician in charge of the chemistry of the various developing solutions.

cherry picker An extremely tall crane topped by a platform used as a camera platform for very high angle shots. See **Simon hoist**.

chest cap (USA) A printed identification caption normally superimposed over the lower third of the screen.

chiaroscuro lighting Use of juxtaposed extreme light and dark areas within a composition to heighten dramatic impact.

chicken wire Wire netting used as a base for constructing scenery and props.

Children's Film & Television Foundation British organisation for sponsoring and promoting children's films.

chinagraph A soft wax pencil used

particularly by film editors to write identifications on film and sound tape.

chinese To close barn doors on a lamp to a narrow horizontal slit, thus restricting the beam of light. Opposite of **English**.

Chinese bus Transport carrying a number of people all of whom are claiming individual travelling allowances.

Chinese dolly Tracking shot in which the camera both pulls back and pans at the same time whilst holding the subject in frame. So-called because the dolly tracks have to be placed at a slant to the subject.

Chinese ticket Free or subsidised fare for which the recipient claims reimbursement at the full rate from his employers.

chip camera Video camera using solid state, light-sensitive silicon pickups instead of camera tubes.

chipmunking (USA) High pitched, chattering voice effect like a cartoon rodent, resulting from a sound tape running at a too fast speed.

chippy A stage carpenter.

chopper shot Picture taken from a helicopter.

choreographer The person in charge of plotting and directing dance sequences.

Christmas tape Compilation tape of out-takes and general mayhem recorded during the year by VT engineers and played back on closed circuit each Christmas.

Christmas tree Trolley used to cart lighting equipment around a stage, so-called because it is usually festooned with cables.

chroma Term used by engineers to describe the intensity of a colour.

chromakey Visual electronic effect using colour (usually blue or yellow) to provide a switching signal for the electronic insertion of a background from a separate source.

chromakey blue Saturated blue colour used for **colour separation overlay** and chromakey effects, as blue is the colour least prominent in human flesh tints.

chrominance 1. The control on a colour monitor or receiver which deals with the saturation of the colours as distinct from the brightness of the image. **2.** The transmitted part of the signal which deals with colour information.

chuck wagon Location catering van.

Chyron Make of electronic character generator used also for simple animation.

cinch marks Scratch marks on film caused by winding the roll too tightly.

cine strip Short test strip of film printed daily by a laboratory and sent to the cameraman daily during a long production as a quality control.

cineaste 1. Someone professionally employed in the film business. **2.** A film buff.

Cinecitta Italian studio complex near Rome.

cinema verité A style of filming in which the camera attempts to capture or simulate real events in real time with minimum camera direction. A common technique on documentary production. A frequent device in drama.

Cinemascope Wide screen film shot on 35mm film with an anamorphic lens offering wide screen aspect ratios.

cinematographer Alternative title to **lighting cameraman.**

cinematography The craft of making moving pictures.

Cinemoid Trade name for coloured filters put in front of studio or stage lighting to create colour effects. See **gel.**

Cinerama Wide screen format involving the projection of three separate images with stereophonic sound.

circuit breaker A master switch for cutting off all electric power to a technical area. An isolator switch.

cladding Board used to cover frames of flats, rostra, etc, in scenic construction.

clamp 1. An electronic circuit used to ensure that the electronic black level is maintained throughout the signal processing. **2.** Device for fixing lights, etc, to scenery.

clapometer Device incorporated into the set of a quiz or talent show which purports to register the volume of audience applause.

clapper boy Junior operative who operates the clapperboard.

clapperboard The board comprising two pieces of wood clapped together which gives visual and audible indications to the film editor how to synchronize sound and picture tracks from the rushes.

clapperloader A second assistant cameraman concerned with loading film magazines and using the clapperboard.

clapsticks A clapperboard.

claw The mechanism in a camera or projector which engages in the sprocket holes of a length of film and drags it through the gate in synchronism with the shutter.

clean feed 1. Continuous recording, free of any commentary, of actuality sound at an event. **2.** A reverse audio feed from a studio to another remote source, i.e. studio output minus the incoming remote source.

clean programme 1. A programme from which sexual innuendo is absent. **2.** A live

clear camera one!

programme successfully transmitted without technical faults.

clear camera one!/ two!/ three! In multi-camera studios, the director's instruction to a camera that it is finished in one scene and should move to frame up its next shot elsewhere.

clear shot! Instruction by a director to someone who is inadvertently in vision.

clearances Technical formalities of ensuring that all legal, contractual and copyright restrictions can be overcome.

clearing stick A long pole used to manœuvre scenery being flown or to adjust lights.

cleat A fitment to which a line is made fast when scenery is being flown.

click track Tape of recorded clicks used as a metronome or a countdown device.

cliffhanger A series or serial in which each episode ends at a moment of unresolved high tension, leaving the audience waiting with baited breath for the next instalment.

clip A short excerpt from a film/programme, sometimes a general description of a cut or trim.

clip-on mike A miniature personal mike which can be clipped unobtrusively on to clothing. See **lapel mike**.

clipboard Hard board to which shot lists, notes, questions, etc, may be affixed. Wielded in vision as symbols of importance by presenters and journalists.

clipping A printed item copied, cut out or quoted from a published reference source.

clipping level The level at which television electronic switches are set to change state, as in adjusting CSO/chromakey or keyed captions.

clock A count-down clock used at the beginning of programmes for timing and identification. May be mechanical or electronically generated.

clog Loss of recording or playback on videotape caused by detached pieces of oxide fouling the tape machine heads. The electronic equivalent of the **hair in the gate** in film.

close down The nightly announcement of the end of transmission by the presentation announcer.

close up (CU) Generally any close shot of an object, but on TV specifically a shot of the whole human face from the top of the head to the base of the neck.

closed circuit television (CCTV) Programme made to be shown internally by an organisation and not intended for broadcast transmission. CCTV is a generally-used term for all kinds of non-broadcast television.

closed set/studio Shooting where the subject matter is so confidential or intimate that the location or studio is banned to all but essential personnel.

closing titles The list of production and technical name credits which comes traditionally at the close of a film or programme.

cloud effect Lantern with a rotating attachment which projects shadows on a scene to simulate passing clouds.

co-axial cable A cable in which the vision or high-frequency signal runs centrally through the cable and is surrounded by a metal sheath which acts as an earth conductor.

co-production A production in which the finances are split between two or more organisations with reciprocal agreements about transmission rights and profits.

coated lens A lens treated to reduce the

amount of reflection from the optics otherwise known as a **bloomed lens**.

cobweb effect Machine which drips rubber solution into a fast-moving fan creating thin strands over a set to simulate cobwebs. Much beloved by directors of horror movies.

cod up 1. To improvise creatively in a way that conceals the lack of response from the audience. **2.** To perform half seriously or to parody.

code numbers See **rubber numbers**.

coder An electronic circuit for combining, for example, the different red, blue and green signals from a camera into a single-coded signal for transmission. See **decoder**.

coding machine (USA) A film rubber numbering machine.

cold To go without preparation or previous rehearsal.

cold light A light such as office fluorescent lighting which resembles general daylight, e.g. without the orange cast of normal tungsten lighting.

cold light illuminator A light box developed for viewing X-ray photographs in hospitals but in TV studios to illuminate film transparencies used as test cards.

cold run A first rehearsal without props, costume or lighting.

collodion Spirit based make-up solution. Flexible collodion is used to fill in or cover wrinkles; inflexible collodion is used for the reverse effect, by contracting the skin or drying to make scars, wrinkles and blemishes.

Collux A trade name of a type of lightmeter which can measure colour temperature as well as intensity.

Colortran A manufacturer of film and television location and studio lights, etc.

colour bias (USA) The effect on colours caused by the transmission path or recording medium of the NTSC television system. Does not apply to PAL or SECAM.

colourizer (USA) A colour synthesizer.

colour balance See **balance**.

colour bars See **bars**.

colour cast Unwanted colour effect caused by reflected light which is not usually noticed by eye, e.g. green light filtered through leaves, red light from a setting sun, etc. Particularly important to watch on skin tones in close-ups.

colour correction The use of a lens filter to compensate for film balanced either for artificial tungsten light or for blue normal daylight, or to filter light from a window or lamp to match existing lighting. Also, to correct electronically a video signal using a device such as a Cox box.

colour item Story of no great topical content purporting to give background or evoke atmosphere; a soft story covering such items as hot air ballooning, cute animals or whatever. Used to fill up airtime by tired news editors.

colour mobile control room (**CMCR**) A mobile control room for controlling a number of cameras and sound on an outside broadcast.

colour response The sensitivity of the eye or electronic pick-up device, e.g. tube or CCD to light of different frequencies (colours).

colour roving eye (**CRE**) See **roving eye**.

colour saturation The degree to which a colour is pure or diluted by white.

colour separation overlay (**CSO**) System using colours to provide a switching signal for a composite picture.

colour synthesizer Facility on a gallery desk to create independently coloured foregrounds, backgrounds and edges to monochrome sources, particularly with graphic captions.

colour temperature A means of describing the colour of light expressed in degrees Kelvin.

colour triad A group of three phosphorus dots, one blue, one green and one red on the face of a conventional TV tube.

column chart Graphic portrayal of statistics in which percentages are illustrated by a rank of vertical, apparently three-dimensional columns.

combined mobile central control room (CMCCR) A mobile control room for co-ordinating a number of outside broadcast vehicles on major events.

combined print See **married print**.

Combo 1. (USA) A VT camera combining an integral recorder, e.g. **Betacam**. See **camcorders. 2.** A musical group .

come down To end a performance or display; term derived from the lowering of a theatre curtain, used mainly by audio-visual designers.

come in over budget/under budget To complete a programme having spent either more or less than the estimated original amount of money, the former being more common than the latter.

comet tailing Effect found on electronic cameras where highlights appear to streak when fast moving objects cross the image.

coming up (USA) Director's warning of impending activity similar to British command '*stand by!*'.

Comité Consultative International des Radiocommunications (CCIR). Standard for audio recording.

commag (combined magnetic sound) Film in which the sound track is printed alongside the picture on a continuous magnetic strip. Once used by TV news film cameramen but replaced by videotape. Still used in amateur film-making (8mm) .

comment Editorial content revealing the speculations of the programme makers. *'Comment is free, facts are sacred.'* C.P. SCOTT Parodied by TV journalists as *'Facts are expensive'*. See **internal balance**.

commentary Scripted words delivered out of vision over a cut film or VT programme.

commentary booth An acoustically treated box at a dubbing theatre where a commentator reads a script to pictures.

commentator 1. Person employed to read commentaries. **2.** A reporter at a live sporting or other outside event giving blow-by-blow description of the occasion.

commercial A television advertisement, typically between twenty seconds and one minute in duration.

commercial break The scheduled break in TV broadcasts to show commercials.

commercial record A recording for public retail sale for which copyright clearances must be made before televisual use.

commissary (USA) A studio canteen.

common junction Times scheduled to enable viewers to switch conveniently between programmes on, e.g. BBC-1 and BBC-2, because they begin at the same time. See also **junction**.

Commonwealth Broadcasting Association Organisation conceived to promote links and co-operation between broadcasting networks in the British Commonwealth countries.

comms van Communications vehicle which accompanies an outside broadcast vehicle and is responsible for the telecommunications links which transmit the signal back to base. Also known as **links van**.

communications satellite Space satellite which receives and retransmits telecommunications signals from earth.

Community Antenna Television (CATV) (USA) System in which a signal is received by a single aerial and then distributed to homes by coaxial cables.

Community TV/Radio 1. Programmes in which a broadcasting authority offers technical facilities and editorial control to outside bodies. **2.** Small local stations run by their own communities.

comopt (common optical) Film with the sound track printed optically alongside the pictures. In early films the sound was recorded optically. Comopt prints are the usual means of distributing films for cinema projection.

compact disc (CD) Small convenient carrier of digitally-recorded sound or vision recorded via a laser scanning system.

compact indium discharge (CID) Type of narrow beam spotlight.

companding Portmanteau word compressing and expanding: the electronic compression and later expansion of an audio signal enabling it to be passed through or recorded upon equipment unable to take the full dynamic range. See **Dolby**.

compatibility The ability of two or more pieces of equipment or picture or sound sources to match each other in performance.

compatible composition Shots composed by

a cameraman so that they may be watched either on a projector or on a domestic television set without loss of any essential part of the action. See **cut-off**.

compeditor A small electrically-driven machine used by film editors to synchronise sound tracks with pictures.

compère A presenter often capable of unrelenting *bonhomie* who talks to celebrities, personalities and stars in quiz or chat shows. See **celebrity, personality, star**.

compilation An assembled sequence of scenes. Specifically a programme involving extracts of archive film, graphics and other sources with little originally-shot material.

complementary angles Composition where separate shots of two or more performers are taken at approximately the same, but opposite angles,'so that they appear to be talking to each other when the shots are cut together.

complementary colours Colours created by mixing two of the primaries (red, blue, green) in equal quantities which, if then combined with a third, create white light, e.g. green + blue = cyan; cyan + red = white; blue + red = magenta; magenta + green = white; red + green = yellow (amber); yellow + blue = white.

complementary picture amplifier A device that produces the complementary colour of any colour at its input by subtracting that colour from white.

complementary shot A shot taken with a matching composition to another in a two-handed interview or dramatic scene.

component video Technique using video recorder with two heads: recorded signal is not decoded in conventional form, but gives a much higher-quality picture.

composite shot Two or more different images appearing on the screen at the same time.

composition The arrangement of picture elements within the frame to achieve a pleasing result by moving performers or scenery, or by selecting a lens or angle of view.

compression The dynamic range of an audio signal being electronically reduced.

compressor Device used to reduce the volume range of sound without giving distortion.

computer editing controller A videotape editing aid where machine functions and audio and video transitions are controlled by a computer.

computer graphics Graphics generated and transmitted directly by using digital computer techniques, instead of artwork.

Comsat, United States Communications Satellite Corporation. US body which regulates satellite telecommunications between the US and foreign organisations.

concentration pattern (USA) The pacing of dramatic structure so that a plot climax is precisely timed to precede immediately a commercial break.

condenser mike A high-quality microphone where sound waves vary the gap between two plates of a capacitor. A voltage is applied between the plates and the resulting very small signal may be amplified as an electrical replica of the original sound waves. Requires a power supply. Also known as **capacitor mike.**

confidence monitoring (USA) Continuous monitoring of the output of a sound tape during a recording by listening to the playback from a head situated after the sound recording head.

console A lighting or sound control desk.

consumer video (USA) Domestic videotape systems.

contact print Photographic print taken from a negative by placing the developed negative in contact alongside the unexposed film stock and running both simultaneously through a printer.

continuity The flow of pictures without jumps in the action or discrepancies in set or costume.

continuity girl Production team member who checks for discrepancies in action. In television this is normally done by the production assistant. Known as **script assistant** in the USA, hence *La Script* in France.

continuity sheet A record kept by the production assistant on location, giving details of continuity to be referred to in subsequent filming and post-production.

continuity suite A small studio from which announcements are made and programme junctions are controlled, usually manned by a single announcer.

continuous printer Mechanical process in which the film being copied and the raw stock are moved through a processing machine in two moving strips. See **step printer**.

contract Legally-binding financial agreement.

contrast gradient The extent to which a film reproduces the contrast ratio, e.g. high contrast gradient film exaggerates extremes of light and shadow.

contrast ratio The range in brightness between the brightest and darkest parts of a scene that can be satisfactorily reproduced by the television system.

contrejour French term for filming towards the light, at its most extreme a silhouette shot.

control

control (USA) The part of an electronic studio where the director, vision mixer, production assistant and certain of the engineers sit during a programme or recording. In the UK, normally called the **gallery**.

control desk The vision mixing panel in a studio together with the talkback facilities, etc, used by the director and production assistant.

control line A private telephone line between source and destination.

control track A continuous signal recorded on videotape to ensure that the tape runs at the correct speed. The electronic equivalent of sprocket holes on film.

controller Senior rank of BBC Management (cf. French *contrôleur* = a ticket collector).

convention Any well-used stylistic approach which the audience accepts as appropriate, e.g. out-of-vision commentary in documentaries

CONTROLLER

or quick drama cutting to imply tension. Many cinematic conventions quickly become clichés.

conversion filter Lens filter used to compensate for the differences between daylight and tungsten artificial light.

convertibility Budgeting term to describe the way in which production cash costs and fixed resource costs may sometimes be interchanged. See **above the line** and **below the line**.

cook The processing of film in the developing bath at a higher than usual temperature.

cookie (USA) Flag mounted in front of a lamp to give the silhouette of trees, branches, clouds etc. Abbreviation for **cucaloris**.

copy Scripted material for inclusion in a topical programme. Also written content of an advertising campaign.

copyright The legal ownership of written words, pictures, photographs, music and almost any material used in a programme for which payment may be due.

copytaker Copy typist responsible for taking down news information dictated by journalists to the newsroom by telephone.

copytaster Sub-editorial figure who receives news information from news agencies, stringers, etc, and selects those which look worthy of further investigation.

copywriter Employee of an advertising agency who devises the content and style of advertisements, particularly the written elements.

core Plastic disc around which a film is wound.

cormorant A type of pan and tilt head for studio or location camera mountings.

corn Secondhand and predictable content for programmes aiming at an undiscriminating mass audience. Material which has lost all originality through repetition.

corpse To be unable to continue a scene due to uncontrollable hilarity.

correspondent Journalist deployed to concentrate on particular subject area. Derived from the era of newspapers when gentlemen of the press were employed in different geographical locations and corresponded with the editor of the journal on matters of local importance.

co-sited **1.** Where separate radio and TV services share the same premises. **2.** Transmitters from two or more broadcasting organisations sharing the same transmitter mast.

costume Theatrical clothing. Also used as the name for the department responsible for costumes. See **frocks, wardrobe**.

CORMORANT

costume drama Drama set in an historical period mainly identified by attention paid to wardrobe and design.

count out Instructions from the gallery to bring an interview or programme to an end. Normally, one minute, thirty seconds, fifteen seconds, ten seconds, wind-up, and cut-throat.

countdown The process of counting into a live transmission by the floor manager and, in the gallery, by the production assistant. Normally, one minute, thirty seconds, twenty seconds, ten seconds counted down to zero.

counterpoint The technique of combining apparently incongruous sounds and pictures to create dramatic effect or impart irony.

cove Curved baseboard used to disguise the join between a cyclorama and the studio floor or conceal a set of ground row lights.

cover shot (USA) See **master shot**.

coverage 1. The manpower and technical resources deployed to make up a story in a news context. 2. The duration devoted to an individual story in a news bulletin.

Cox box One of many electronic colour corrective devices.

crab dolly Low camera chassis with steerable wheels capable of movement in any direction.

crab/crabbing The action of moving a camera sideways, crabwise, as opposed to tracking (USA **trucking**) back and forwards.

cradle dolly (USA) Camera dolly in the form of a platform running along precision tracks.

crane A large camera mounting which can elevate, depress and jib the camera. Most commonly used in studio, sound stages or film lots. See **jib, dolly, cherry picker**.

crank gain Turning up video camera's

amplification to compensate for low light levels. Similarly on sound to boost low sound levels.

crash in/out Occurs when there is a misjudgement of time at a programme junction so that a director has to cut instantly at the end of one programme into the beginning of another.

crash start (USA) A pre-title sequence.

crash zoom Extremely fast zoom into an object to give a startling dramatic effect.

crawl 1. Method of superimposing captions in which the words appear to move across the screen. **2.** (USA) Roller caption normally used for credits.

creative director Employee of an advertising agency in overall charge of the visual elements in a campaign, including the commissioning of television commercials.

creative geography Technique for giving an illusion of time and space, e.g. actor walks to studio window and opens curtains before a cut to a shot of the Eiffel tower, thus giving the impression that the whole action takes place in Paris.

credits Names of participating production and technical contributors, normally at the end of a programme. Front credits are usually restricted to programme titles and names of writers, though actors are also often front credited in American productions as a build up to the first commercial break.

creep in/out Move a camera towards or away from the subject at a barely perceptible speed.

creeper A very low-angle dolly used in studios. Commonly known as **VLAD**.

creeping sync The result of a fault in the synchronising of a camera or recorder, or during sound transfer in which sound and picture progressively drift apart. Also known as **slipping sync**.

crew The team of technicians responsible to the director for camera, sound and lights. In studios the term is frequently limited to the camera operators, or camera and sound operators working on the studio floor.

crib card/camera card The written sequence of shots for each individual studio camera. Normally attached to a holder on the side of the camera. Also, a synonym for **idiot board cards** for actors.

crimper A hairdresser.

cropping 1. Trimming the area of a photographic or television image by excising or masking off unwanted areas. 2. Loss of parts of a picture on the edge of an image, usually due to overscanning by a TV receiver. See **domestic cut-off**.

cross-cut Alternately intercutting between two scenes or two opposing camera angles.

cross-fade One shot mixed to another as the outgoing image fades to black and the incoming one fades up from black.

cross-lighting Lighting predominantly from one side of a set, e.g. to simulate moonlight through a window.

cross-shooting The normal technique for shooting interviews on two cameras in which the participants face each other and the two opposing cameras take complementary matching positions whilst not getting each other in shot.

cross-talk Effect similar to crossed telephone lines in which extraneous conversations leak through to sound in the studio or radio microphone, e.g. from taxi or police radio or talkback from an adjacent studio. May also occur on electronic pictures when an extraneous image appears low level behind the main picture.

crossing the line A fault in direction which occurs when a scene is shot from two opposite sides so that the characters appear to keep reversing their positions in relation to each other when the pictures are cut together. See **line of action** .

crushing black/white The result of the contrast in a scene being so great that the camera is unable to resolve the darkest or brightest parts of the scene and detail is lost.

crystal lock System by which pictures and sounds, running in an unconnected camera and sound recorder, can be kept in synchronisation by use of an accurate quartz crystal speed control.

crystal microphone A cheap low-quality microphone relying on a small piezo electric crystal to produce an electrical signal.

crystal sync Describes the way in which the film camera and its tape recorder are synchronised without the need of a cable connection between them.

cucaloris See **cookie.**

cue Aural or visual signal given to an artist to speak or move.

cue card 1. A camera card. 2. Card with parts of the script marked on it either concealed about a set or held up next to the camera, to help the memories of tired or emotional performers. See **idiot card, jumbo card, crib card.**

cue dot A visible set of dots usually made by making small perforations at the top of frames in new film to indicate that the film is coming to an end. Used to tell cinema projectionists when to change projectors. Can also be electronically produced on VT to signal an approaching time junction and by network presentation areas to cue in live programmes or commercial breaks.

cue light 1. A light in a studio or dubbing theatre used to tell a presenter when to speak. 2. The light on an electronic studio camera indicating that it is the one on air.

cue tone Electronically-generated tone to mark the beginning of a new track on a sound recording.

cue track An additional low-quality audio track on quad videotape sometimes used for talk-back.

cumulative time (USA) Total allocated time of a programme including commercial breaks.

current affairs Topical TV programmes supposedly concerned with the political, social and economic problems of the day.

cut To drop script lines from a performance or sections from a programme.

cut! Command by the director to the unit that a shot is finished.

cut bank Bank of switches on a vision console on which the vision mixer is actually cutting from one camera to another. In order to achieve a mix or other effect a second bank of switches duplicating the first will be needed.

cut editing Videotape editing method of physically cutting and joining the tape together. Sometimes used to describe two-machine VT editing where cuts only are possible.

cut key bar A bank of buttons on certain types of vision mixers that enables direct cuts to a source regardless of the fader positions.

cut on action The artistic principle of editing pictures at the moment when a performer makes a move, so maintaining the flow of the action and disguising any jumps or continuity faults.

cut story Complete, edited item.

cut throat Signal given to a speaker by a floor manager who draws a finger across his throat to indicate that an interview/script must be brought to an immediate close.

cut-back (USA) Editing device of returning to a general view of the action after one or more close shots.

cut-in A shot inserted into the main action to emphasize a dramatic moment, e.g. a big close up cut into a mid-shot. The opposite in intention to a cutaway shot.

cut-off The part of a transmitted picture lost through imperfect adjustment of domestic television sets, and aspect ratio differences between transmitted picture and receiver cathode ray tube.

cut-out A foil or card cut into shape and placed in front of a light to create shadow effects.

cutaway A shot of something other than the main action used either to draw the audience's attention away to something new or by the picture editor to cover bad continuity or a jump cut.

cutaway questions Questions from an interview repeated by the interviewer to camera after the departure of the guest to facilitate smooth editing. See **noddy**, **reverse**.

cutter (USA) A film or VT editor.

cutting copy The assembly of the film compiled by the film editor from the rushes. Normally used up to and including the dub and from which negative cutting is done to compile the final negative for an answer print.

cutting room The room in which the film editor works.

cyan The blue/green mixture of light

complementary to red. See **complementary colours**.

cyc light Soft light used to illuminate a cyclorama from above as opposed to from below by a ground row.

cyc track A permanent rail around a studio from which the cyclorama can be suspended.

cycle one complete wave of alternating current when amplitude and direction have returned to starting point.

cycles per second (cps) An obsolete term now replaced by **Hertz**. AC current in Europe is normally 50 Hz, in the USA 60 Hz.

cyclorama Often abbreviated **cyc** (*pron*. sike). A curved studio backdrop on to which background lighting can be projected.

cygnet Lightweight camera pan and tilt head.

D
AD See **digital audio disc.**
DBS See **direct broadcasting by satellite.**
dB See **decibel.**

DBE See **departmental budget estimate.**

DC See **direct current.**

DEL See **direct exchange line.**

DFI See **director's fresh instruction.**

DIN See **Deutsche Industrie Norm**

DG See **director general.**

DJ See **disc jockey.**

DOIL See **days off in lieu.**

DR despatch rider.

DT See **dynamic tracking.**

DVE See **digital video effects.**

D mount Screw thread lens mount commonly used by 8mm cameras.

D Notice An official warning to journalists listing subjects which might be of a security or politically sensitive nature under the Official Secrets Act.

dailies (USA) Film **rushes.**

dampen To reduce the reverberation of a studio acoustic by introducing sound-absorbent screens or curtains, soft furnishings, or egg boxes nailed to the wall.

damper Covering for a drum skin which enables a drummer to mime frantically to a backing track without making real sounds.

dark room Room with controllable illumination used for the safe handling of photographic materials.

dark stage Early description of an enclosed film studio lit entirely by artificial light.

Date (USA) System for the simultaneous transmission of stereophonic radio and television programmes. See **simulcast.**

daubing Scene painting technique of dabbing paint of a different tone on to a coloured background with a paint-soaked rag. Used to suggest textures like old stucco.

day-for-night Sequences shot in daylight hours using lighting effects and filters to create a night-time atmosphere.

daylight film Film whose sensitivity is corrected to give a correct rendition of colours exposed to ordinary daylight, as opposed to tungsten film which is balanced for domestic artificial light.

daylight loading Film loaded on to a spool with flanges which protect the outer film from fogging. Normal for short rolls of film used for news and for amateur use.

days off in lieu (DOIL) Term used by television technicians for days off given in lieu of, or in addition to, overtime or penalty payments. See **time off in lieu (toil)**.

daytime TV Continuous broadcasting from the end of breakfast TV in the early morning until the beginning of the early evening schedules. See **in-filling**.

De Wolfe British publishers of recorded background music and effects.

de-bag Remove wrinkles from around the eyes by application of make-up.

de-rig The striking of a set or dismantling of technical apparatus.

dead An acoustic which is totally non-reverberative and therefore lacks any sense of perspective.

dead end End of a studio with the least reverberating acoustic.

dead side The side of a **directional mike** pointed away from the sound source.

deadline The point in time by which the script of a production has to be completed. Derived from the American Civil War prisoner-of-war camps where prisoners were shown a perimeter line beyond which guards shot to kill.

deaf aid Small earpiece worn by presenters on live programmes through which the gallery can talk to them whilst the programme is on air. Also called a hearing aid. See **switched talkback**.

decay time The time it takes for a reverberation of a sound to die away, e.g. echo in a room.

decibel (dB) A unit for measuring the volume of sound or vision.

decoder 1. A device for recovering the constituent parts of a signal coded or combined for transmission, recording, etc. **2.** Device inside a television set to reconstitute the three primary colours from the coded signal. See **encoding**.

decor (USA) Set design or dressing.

deejay (DJ) Abbreviation for **disc jockey**.

deep focus shot Shot of great depth of field in which characters or objects in the extreme background remain unnaturally in the same sharp focus as those in the foreground.

defamation Broadcast or printed material which damages the reputation of a person or organisation and therefore actionable in law.

definition The degree to which fine differences of sound or picture detail can be distinguished.

defocus-focus Effect produced by defocusing a camera on one shot and then focusing up from an indecipherable blur on a second shot with a mix in between. Once a popular cinema technique for suggesting a lapse of time, flashback or dream sequence.

degaussing The electrical de-magnetization of metal objects e.g. audio/video record/replay heads, colour television tubes, etc.

delay time The time taken for a signal to pass through a circuit, piece of equipment or over a transmission link. Sometimes used deliberately, e.g. to produce an echo-like effect.

delayed broadcast Programme recorded as live with the intention of retransmission at a precise later time.

demo disc/tape Pilot recording made by a musical group for demonstration or publicity purposes but not for retail distribution.

demodulation The removal of the carrier signal from transmitted or recorded material.

densitometer Film laboratory apparatus for measuring the colour density on a frame of film.

density The measure of image light or blackness on a film.

departmental budget estimate (DBE) BBC TV term for a detailed estimate of production costs submitted for approval by a producer before work can begin.

depress To push down a camera on its pedestal and lower the lens height.

depth of field The distance between the nearest and furthest objects of a scene which are in focus. Varied by the use of different lenses or apertures.

depth of focus Measure of the distance between the nearest and farthest point at which the image plane is in focus.

desaturate To bleach out colour intensity to pastel tones, e.g. the dilution of red tones to pink.

designer The person responsible for creating, drawing and installing a set on a location, lot, studio or stage. Specialist designers are responsible for costume, graphics, fights and special effects.

desk 1. A name for any of the separate control consoles in a studio technical area. 2. Division of a newsroom dealing with a specific area of responsibility, e.g. foreign desk, the group of journalists responsible for monitoring stories from abroad.

desk mike Microphone placed upon or built into a desk used by a studio presenter.

desk overlay Chromakey system operated in a studio gallery by a separate electronic effects operator instead of the vision mixer.

Deutsche Industrie Norm (DIN) German standards organisation. Specifically a scale for rating film speed or sensitivity; an alternative to ASA/ISO rating.

developing shot A complex camera shot in which the camera moves to encapsulate a complete action without the necessity of intercutting.

development 1. Chemical process which reveals the latent image on an exposed piece of film. 2. The following of a continuous piece of action or a continuous movement on one camera. 3. The evolution of a plot or story line.

diabolo Suspended roller transporting a loop of film in a processing laboratory.

diagonal splice Method of splicing film with a diagonal cut instead of a straight one in order to make a stronger join and minimise any clicking on the film sound track.

dialogue Scripted spoken words in a dramatised programme.

dialogue equalizer Sound desk facility for adjusting the perspective of voices for balance or dramatic purposes.

dialogue replacement The post-synchronisation of words which are repeated to match lip movements on original pictures, where the original sound is unsatisfactory or in a foreign language. Normal procedure in feature films. See **automatic dialogue replacement, looping**.

diaphragm The camera iris. The adjustable aperture which controls the amount of light passing through a lens.

diary story A news story which can be predicted and set up in advance, e.g. a public event, state visit, anniversary or the like, noted in the newsroom diary.

diascope An attachment for the front of a camera to enable precise measurements of optical aberrations, camera sensitivity, etc.

dichroic filter An optical filter that is frequency sensitive, i.e. it passes some colours and reflects others.

diesel rig Apparatus burning a mixture of diesel fuel, petrol, etc, used to create heavy smoke effects.

differential gain Distortion produced when the television signal is passed through a non-linear system, having different gain characteristics at high/low signal amplitudes.

diffraction lens Special effects lens giving a rainbow effect on the highlights.

diffuser A frosted screen or mesh in front of a lamp or a camera lens which diffuses light or softens a picture outline.

diffusion filter Lens filter which gives a slight soft focus or halo effect. See **fog filter**.

digigrade A computerized method of recording and recalling grading settings of film on its transfer to videotape.

Digiprompt A proprietory prompting system using a special word processor.

digital audio disc (DAD) Single-sided audio disc 4.7-inch diameter with a laser-scanned track running from the centre to the outside. See **compact disc.**

digital frame store An electronic device that uses a computer to store one single frame of picture for subsequent read-out, either directly as a still frame or as a manipulated picture, e.g. upside down, reverse, reduced in size, display.

digital read out A read-out in figures instead of an analogue system like the sweep arm of a clock.

digital recording Sound or pictures converted to digital signals before recording and playback. A major advantage over analogue recording is the ability to copy on to subsequent generations with no loss of quality.

digital remastering Re-recording in digital form from an original analogue recording for subsequent copying. A common means of up-grading and re-issuing old commercial discs.

digital signal Signal consisting of two discrete levels. Can carry a code to represent an analogue quantity and is very resistant to noise.

digital telecine Machine which converts images from a moving picture tape into a digital picture memory store for later retrieval as a still frame or similar effect.

digital video effects (DVE) **1.** Digital electronic picture effects box. **2.** The generic term for all digital electronic picture manipulation.

dimmer A control for the brightness of stage or studio lamps.

dimmer bank A number of variable resistance

units grouped together on a lighting console and used to control lights.

DIN plug Connecting plugs commonly used with film and electronic equipment.

dingle shot A shot in which a piece of vegetation or the like is hung in front of the lens to give depth to a composition or give an impression of rusticity.

diopter A frontal attachment to a lens used to achieve extra close-up facilities.

diorama A detailed three-dimensional scenic model familiar in museum designs but sometimes used as a miniature model set for special effects filming.

dip sound! Instruction by a director to a sound engineer to lower the volume or take out music or effects in a programme.

dipole The active element of an aerial.

direct broadcasting by satellite (DBS) The transmission of signals from source to a receiver via a satellite without use of traditional ground-based transmitter or masts.

direct current (DC) Electric current moving in one direction only.

direct exchange line (DEL) A telephone line from a gallery or outside broadcast which gives direct access to the public telephone system.

directional mike A microphone, usually a gun mike, which picks up sound only from a very narrow axis along the direction in which it is pointed.

director The creative executive in charge of the performances of artists, direction of camera crews and post-production. A role whose definition varies from production to production, but is normally the key to its artistic success. See **brother-in-law**.

director general (DG) Chief executive of the British Broadcasting Corporation.

director of photography Title adopted by lighting cameramen who use an assistant as camera operator. See **cinematographer, lighting cameraman**.

director's fresh instruction (DFI) The euphemistic version. DFI was originally an electricians' term used for inexperienced directors who kept changing their minds. Now used universally to mean a change of plan.

dirty up Artificially age a set, usually by using various powders and sprays. See **blow down**.

disc A gramophone record.

disc jockey (DJ) Radio term for person who plays a series of records and chatters between them.

discharge lamp Lamp which uses an electric arc rather than a heated filament.

discontinuous recording A recorded multi-camera video programme in which the individual scenes/sequences are recorded separately with breaks between and then edited together.

discotheque In Britain normally a club or dance hall playing recorded music, usually abbreviated to disco. In Latin countries refers also to a **record library**.

dish A saucer-shaped aerial, part of any telecommunications link. See **parabolic aerial**.

dish mike A saucer-shaped reflector surrounding a microphone which concentrates and distinguishes distant or indistinct sounds. Particularly used in natural history sound recordings.

Disney dust Effect achieved optically at the

film printing stage for glittering stars, fairy dust or whatever. See **glitter**.

dissolve The gradual mixing of the end of one shot into the beginning of the next produced by overlapping a fade-out with a fade-in.

Distagons Range of fast film camera lenses manufactured by Zeiss.

distant shot (USA) See **long shot**.

distortion An aberration in a signal introduced by equipment as a result of a design fault or malfunction.

distribution amplifier An amplifier employed to feed one signal to several destinations without loss of signal strength and without mutual interference.

dock The area adjacent to a studio or stage where scenery is temporarily stored.

docu-drama (USA) See **drama-doc**.

documentary An interpretative feature programme about a single factual subject. *'The creative interpretation of actuality'* John Grierson.

Dolby Patented noise reduction system used with sound recorders for both domestic and professional equipment.

dolly **1.** A mounting on which a camera may be moved either on wheels or on rails. Pushed by a grip. **2.** (USA) Common generic term for many sorts of camera movement. See **trucking**.

domestic cut-off The part of a transmitted picture which is lost due to the overscanning of the normal home TV receiver or by transmitting cinema films of a different aspect ratio from the TV screen.

dominant shot A shot, normally from a low angle, favouring one artist who is thus made to look dominant over another, e.g. one appears to look down on the other, who conversely looks up and appears submissive.

door flat Functional stage flat constructed to simulate a doorway.

doorstepping News technique where a journalist or crew are despatched to wait outside a building in the hope of filming those entering or leaving and intimidating them into making statements.

dope Film cement.

dope sheets A written record of a shoot and any special editing or post-production requirements, normally filled in daily by the assistant film cameraman. Also written catalogued details in a film library.

dottle Scenic painting technique for simulating texture on a flat surface by dotting or dabbing colours in a *pointilliste* style.

double Stand-in for main actor, generally for stunt purposes or in very wide shots for economic reasons.

double action An edit in which part of the action in one shot is repeated in the incoming shot. Usually an editing mistake but sometimes used for effect.

double band projector Double-headed film projector, carrying both picture and the separate magnetic sound track in synchronism.

double broad Two 1,000 watt lamps mounted in tandem to give soft illumination to a wide area.

double bubble Overtime paid at double-time rates. See **bubble**.

double carousels Twin slide projectors used for sequences of stills where quick cut or slow fade picture changes are required.

double chain System of running film on two

rolls on two telecine machines to achieve mixes between images.

double clad Stage flattage constructed to be viewed from both sides.

double exposure Effect by causing the light to fall on the same piece of film on two occasions resulting in superimposed combined images.

double feature Cinema programme offering two main films in a single showing.

double framing Each frame is printed two or three times to slow down the action. A means, for example, of removing the comic jerkiness of early hand-cranked movies for 25 frames per second TV transmission. Also known as **step printing**.

double perf/perforation stock Film stock with double perforations, e.g. sprocket holes down both edges.

double system Sepmag system for cameras and projectors normally used in television.

double take Reaction movement by a performer followed immediately by a more emphatic or overplayed second reaction to indicate astonishment or delayed comprehension. Used generally for comic effect.

double-ender A cable with either two male or two female plugs. See **sex changer**.

double-headed projector A projector capable of projecting film with a separate magnetic sound track. Amateur/cinema projectors which use **com-opt** or **commag** film are described as single-headed.

double-sided tape Transparent tape with adhesive on both surfaces, much used in graphics and by floor managers to attach light objects to sets.

down music/sound! (USA) Order to dip, fade

or take out recorded sound.

down-the-line The technique of conducting an interview with the interviewer in one studio and the guest in another, usually during a live topical programme.

downstage The part of a theatre proscenium stage nearest to the audience or of a sound set nearest to the camera.

downstream keyer An overlay switch on the output of a vision mixer used particularly for name supers.

drama-doc/documentary Dramatic reconstruction using actors to recreate an historic event. The source of much dispute about the difference between factual and imaginative programmes as well as clashes between broadcasters and politicians. See **faction**.

drapes Curtains used as a backdrop or to conceal parts of sets which might distract from the picture composition. Black velour drapes are the commonest type used.

dress To adorn a set with moveable objects, paintings or furniture to give detail and verisimilitude.

dress rehearsal A final or penultimate rehearsal of artists complete with costume and props.

dress run A full **dress rehearsal**.

dresser Operative of a TV costume department working directly with an actor or actress to fit and adjust costume. A theatrical valet.

dressing 1. Fitting or changing actors' costumes. **2.** Setting properties and furniture in to a studio set.

dressing plan Studio plan with positions of all furniture and props marked on it.

dressing props Properties used to enhance a set design which are essentially portable, e.g. clocks, candelabra, furniture, flowers, etc.

dressing room A specially-equipped room for actors and actresses to change costume and make-up.

drop Vertical suspended curtains or painted cloth.

drop-out A fault on magnetic sound or videotapes when a signal is abruptly lost due to a tape imperfection. See **clog**.

drop-shadow A way of highlighting lettering, either by graphic artwork or by modifying the electronic signal to give the impression of three-dimensional lettering illuminated vertically.

dry To be unable, through complete panic or temporary amnesia, to deliver lines or remember what comes next in an unscripted programme or interview.

dry hire Hire of technical facilities without operational personnel. Opposite of **wet hire**.

dry ice Blocks of frozen carbon dioxide used to create low lying mist or smoke effects.

dry run Rehearsal on set by actors with the technical crew simply observing the cues and moves but without any equipment operating.

dry transfer (USA) Adhesive lettering applied to card by rubbing. See **Letraset**.

dual gauge projector A projector capable of showing both standard eight and super-eight films.

dual standard receiver TV set capable of working in more than one system, e.g. both PAL and SECAM.

dub To copy sound or vision from one source to another. Commonly used to describe the process of copying sounds and words on to a film or VT print at a dubbing theatre. From the French *doubler*, to copy.

dub editing The technique of sound or picture editing on tape whereby the required sequences are selected and copied in order on to another tape. Distinct from **cut editing.**

dubbing chart Sheets of paper drawn up by a picture editor and the assistant to give a pictorial representation of where the sound tracks should be played in by a dubbing mixer.

dubbing mixer The sound technician responsible for the sound mix of a film.

dubbing script Commentary script marked in film footages, seconds or timecode references from which a presenter reads at a film or videotape dub.

dubbing theatre The studio where sound and commentary are mixed to make a final sound track.

ducker/ducking (USA) Device which automatically reduces the level of a background sound channel when the main sound channel exceeds a preset level — much used by disk jockeys to dip the sound of a record when they speak and raise it during pauses.

duct Channel constructed between technical areas to take permanent cable runs.

dump 1. To transfer film or videotape from one format to another prior to editing or transmission. **2.** To transfer information from one computer disc to another.

duopoly Description of the UK broadcasting system in which access to TV transmission was effectively divided between the BBC and the IBA.

dupe 1. To copy a film or tape. **2.** A copy film negative usually taken from a positive print, e.g.

a film editor wishing to cut a piece of library film into specially shot film would need a dupe print for the cutting copy and also a dupe negative for the final print.

duplexer Machine through which a pair of videotape machines are routed to a single destination.

duration Exact length of a programme or an item within one.

Dutch angle See **canted shot**.

Dutch take A pretend take in which no film actually passes through the camera, used as a trick to save film by directors faced with nervous or obstructive interviewees.

Dutchman Strip used to conceal the joins in flats.

dynamic mike A non-powered, pressure-operated microphone.

dynamic range The range of volume of a sound, e.g. from a musical instrument, between the highest peak and the quietest whispers which can be recorded and reproduced.

dynamic tracking (DT) The automatic following of a magnetic track by video heads at non-standard tape speeds to achieve high-quality variable speed or still pictures. See **autoscan tracking (AST)**.

EBCU Script abbeviation for **extra big close-up**.

EBU See **European Broadcasting Union**.

ECC Electronic camera coverage (USA). See **electronic news gathering**.

ECU Extreme close-up. See **big close-up**.

EETPU See **Electrical Engineering Trades and Plumbing Union**.

EFP See **electronic film/field production**.

ELCB See **earth leakage circuit breaker**.

ELS See **extreme long shot**.

EM See **engineering manager**.

EMX See **engineering manual exchange**.

ENG See **electronic news gathering**.

Ext. Script abbreviation for **exterior** scenes.

EVF See **electronic viewfinder**.

E-flex A digital device for producing electronic visual effects.

eagle A 60-foot mobile tower used to mount aerials for radio links from an outside broadcast.

Ealing Comedies Series of British comic feature films produced during the late 1940's and 1950's by the Ealing Studios, whilst under the ownership of the J Arthur Rank organisation.

Ealing Studios West London film studios owned by the BBC.

earphones Headphones, cans.

earpiece intercom (USA) Switched talkback.

earth leakage circuit breaker (ELCB) Device which cuts off the power in the event of an electrical fault causing current to flow from live to earth.

Eastman colour A negative/positive film stock manufactured by Kodak.

echo The repetition of a sound caused by the reflection of sound waves. See **sound**

reverberation, delay time, live acoustic.

echo-plate chamber Chamber containing metal plates into which sound is channelled to increase the reverberation and give a hollow, echoing effect.

Eclair A French manufacturer of film equipment, particularly lightweight cameras for mute filming.

Eclair mounting A robust proprietory camera dolly suitable for lightweight video or film cameras.

edge caption generator Electronic device for giving an approximate three-dimensional effect to simple black and white captions.

edge fogging Fault caused by light penetrating the edges of badly wound film.

edge numbers The numbers printed by the manufacturer along the edges of film stock to make it possible to identify each frame of print and negative. Used by negative cutters to match the cutting copy to the negative before producing an answer print.

edging Electronic addition of black outlines to white lettering or objects to achieve prominence. Occasionally an electronic fault on a camera.

edit A cut between two shots or scenes.

edit controller A panel giving control of machine functions and edit instructions to two or more videotape machines.

edit decision list Video display of numbers of cuts, duration and tape numbers on a computer-controlled videotape editing suite.

edit pair Two videotape machines connected together for the simple cutting of sound and pictures. For sophisticated editing, three-machine editing is required.

Editec 1. A patented edit controller on Ampex

quadruplex videotape machines. **2.** An instant editing technique in which scenes are recorded in sequence, without post-production, by rolling back the tape at the end of a successful take and pressing the record button at the beginning of the next scene.

editing 1. Process of assembling sounds and images in the required sequences. **2.** The process of refining or rewriting the words in written scripts.

editing machine/bench The table at which a film editor works, which has transports for picture and sound track with a small projection screen and loudspeaker. Generally referred to by specific manufacturers' names, e.g. Steenbeck, Moviola.

editor 1. The creative technician who cuts or assembles film or tape. **2.** The executive in charge of the content of a series of television programmes.

editor of the day One of a team of senior journalists working in rotation individually responsible for a complete news programme.

editorial content Slant implying a judgement or comment in addition to the factual content of a report.

editorials Meetings prior to a programme which decide content and structure.

effects bank Battery of buttons on a vision mixing console specifically dedicated to creating trick or special effects.

effects filter Filter mounted on the front of a camera lens to create special distortions of the image.

effects track Composite track taken to a dub which contains sound effects, but neither music nor sync dialogue.

eggy/egg on face An awkward moment due to a technical fault or operational hitch resulting in a performer being stranded in vision looking ridiculous.

Eidophor System of back projection used in studios, which accepts any synchronous video source.

eight millimetre (8mm) Smallest gauge cine film introduced for amateur use in 1932.

eighty-five Filter used by cameramen shooting outdoors with film stock balanced for interior (tungsten) light.

Ektachrome A reversal film stock manufactured by Kodak.

Electret microphone Small, capacitor-type lapel microphone.

Electrical Engineering Trades and Plumbing Union (EETPU) The main trade union for electricians.

electromagnetic mike A moving coil microphone.

electron beam The stream of electrons fired down a cathode-ray tube by an electron gun at a target or phosphor screen.

electron gun The device used to fire an electron beam down a camera or display tube.

electronic camera coverage (ECC) (USA) See **electronic news gathering.**

electronic cinematography The use of video post-production techniques in hybrid film/video feature film productions.

electronic cue dot See **cue dot.**

electronic editing General term for videotape editing which involves copying shots in the required sequence from one tape to another without physically cutting the tape. See **assemble editing, insert editing.**

electronic effects Any effect from simple wipes to complex effects which are generated purely electronically instead of through optical film effects or animated graphics. See also **opticals**.

electronic field or film production (EFP) Basically a BBC term for location shooting with video cameras, often using more than one camera.

electronic film conforming The transfer of videotape to film with in-vision timecode for editing on a film bench prior to final on-line editing. An attempt to combine the basic aspects of film and videotape.

electronic journalism (USA) Alternative term for **electronic newsgathering**.

electronic news gathering (ENG) The use of video cameras in a news context with minimum sized crews. Widely used to describe video, as opposed to film, location shooting.

electronic newsroom Newsroom in which journalists send their reports, via word processors, directly to a script printer and electronic prompting device on the studio floor.

electronic still store. See **frame store**.

electronic studio A TV studio permanently equipped with electronic cameras and ancillary equipment for the recording or transmission of TV programmes.

electronic video recording (USA) Another of the many terms invented to try to distinguish shooting on videotape from shooting on film.

electronic viewfinder (EVF) A small TV monitor connected to a film or VT camera enabling the director to view the action without looking through the camera viewfinder.

Elemac-Octopus A make of camera dolly,

running on wheels or rails, capable of carrying a jib arm and widely used in film and TV.

elements The individual glass components of a composite lens.

elephant's foot Wooden box shaped like a truncated pyramid used by grips to support rails, equipment and short cameramen.

elevate To raise a camera vertically on its pedestal to increase the lens height.

elevation The calculation of the height of a scenic construction in relation to the camera angles by which it is to be shot. The vertical aspect of a set.

Elstree North London suburb site of the first proper British film studios and subsequently the British Hollywood.

Emmy Leading American prizes for television programmes awarded by the Academy of Television Arts and Sciences.

emulsion Coating of silver bromide or silver chloride on a film which is light sensitive.

emulsion in Film wound normally with the emulsion side facing inwards.

emulsion out Film wound with the emulsion side facing towards the outside of the roll.

emulsion speed Indication of the sensitivity of the emulsion on unexposed film generally measured in degrees ISO, ASA or DIN.

encoder The device that combines the red, green and blue signals from a camera. See **coder, decoder.**

encoding The combining of the original red, green and blue signals from a camera into one composite signal for onward transmission.

end board A clapperboard held upside down and used at the end of a take to give the editor a synchronisation point. Employed when it has been impossible to use a board at the start of a shot.

end titles The credits at the conclusion of a programme.

end-out/tail-out Describes a roll of film which has not been rewound and therefore will be back to front if put on an editing machine or on a projector.

engineering manager (EM) The engineer in charge of any outside broadcast.

Engineering Manual Exchange (EMX) A telephone exchange strictly for local communications used amongst engineers on an outside broadcast.

English To close the barn doors in front of a lamp to create a vertical slit. Opposite of a Chinese or horizontal slit effect.

Enterprises Abbreviation for BBC Enterprises, the commercial company of the BBC, responsible for the sales and distribution of its programmes, records, books and magazines.

epic Dramatic production usually characterised by the size of its cast, the complexity of its narrative and the volume of its sound track. Frequently set in some romantic, historical context.

epidiascope A device for overhead projection of transparencies on to a screen in lecture theatres, etc.

epilogue Now defunct end to a night's transmission featuring a short, moral think-piece or sermon.

episode An instalment of a soap opera, situation comedy or drama serial in which part of a continuing narrative is presented.

equal air time Arrangements whereby party political broadcasts or appearances by politicians in the run-up to an election are allotted in proportion to the proportion of seats they hold in the House of Commons.

equaliser **1.** An electronic device for restoring the quality of pictures or sound that have deteriorated through a transmission link.
2. Frequency correction inherent in a vision or sound tape recorder.

Equity /British Actors' Equity British actors' trade union.

erase/wipe To eliminate the recorded electromagnetic information on a sound or videotape.

erase head The first head that a tape passes after leaving the feed spool on a tape recorder. It clears the tape of all unwanted, previously recorded material when the machine is recording.

essential information area Part of a studio monitor which is masked to simulate the loss of image around the edges usual on a domestic TV receiver. See **domestic cut-off**.

establishing shot A shot normally placed at the beginning of a scene or interview implying a readily identifiable geographical relationship.

European Broadcasting Union (EBU) Professional association and programme exchange body including broadcasting corporations from Europe and adjacent areas.

Eurovision News Exchange International system whereby TV organisations relay and exchange news stories daily.

Exchequer levy Tax upon the advertising profits of the IBA companies.

exciter lamp Small intense lamp which converts light waves into sound in an optical sound film projector or editing machine.

executive producer Person responsible for several productions simultaneously, though rarely actively involved in the detailed artistic process of more than one. The overall production boss.

expand Electronic digital video effect in which the image is distorted by stretching sideways or vertically.

exploitation films Films made with an eye for a passing fashion with less concern for quality than for making a quick buck. Those with a heavy erotic element are often called sex-ploitation movies. See **sexploitation, schlock**.

exposure 1. The amount of light allowed to pass through the lens iris to the emulsion to achieve the desired picture. **2.** Publicity in the media, either of a person or a subject.

exposure meter A meter used by cameramen to measure both incident and reflected light.

exposure value A ratio of film speed to aperture.

expressionism Style of dramatic drama in which lighting, art direction and acting styles are used non-naturalistically to convey psycho-logical atmosphere and impose a mood on the viewer. A favoured style of the German cinema between the World Wars.

extension eyepiece Optical extension tube made to fit a camera eyepiece for ease of operation.

extension tube Rigid metal tube between the lens and the body of the camera which distances the lens from the film to facilitate close-up work.

External Services BBC radio services for overseas listeners, comprising the World Service in English and national and regional services in other languages.

other languages.

extra A performer in a group or crowd scene who appears in the background but is not individually directed. Those who receive specific instructions are classified as walk-ons by Union agreement. Also known as **grazing props, supporting artistes.**

extra big close-up (EBCU) Rarely used term to describe a very close shot of an object or a shot of a detail of the human face.

extreme close-up (ECU) See **big close-up**.

extreme long shot (ELS) A panoramic shot with figures too distant for ready identification.

eye lights Reflections of lamps from the eyes, giving apparent vivacity to portraits.

eyeline The direction in which a performer appears to be looking in relation to the camera and other performers.

expenses/exes Creative accountancy at a personal level.

extro See **outro**.

F DU See **fade down and up.**

FM See **frequency modulation** or **floor manager.**

FOC See **father of the chapel.**

FOM See **film operations manager.**

FS, full shot (USA). See **long shot.**

fps See **feet/frames per second.**

FSB See **forty-second burst.**

FSZ Piece of equipment for electronically synchronising a cine camera to electronic TV equipment.

FX Script abbreviation for effects played in studio or a film dub which are neither music nor dialogue. See **sound effects.**

f-number Expression of lens size arrived at by dividing the focal length by the diameter of the open diaphragm.

f-stop Stops on the iris control ring of a camera expressing on a logarithmic scale the amount of light entering a camera, e.g. 2.8, 3.5, 5.6, 8, 11, 16, 22.

face tone Mean light level of a human face under illumination. These tones are most important when balancing the colours in a television studio.

facilities man (USA) A **stagehand.**

facility fee Fee paid to an organisation or member of the public for the use of premises or general inconvenience caused by filming.

facility house A freelance studio offering post-production facilities, hire of crews and equipment to broadcast companies, particularly small production companies, as well as serving industrial films and commercials.

facility trip A trip organised for publicity purposes offered free to members of a production team. See **freebie, swan.**

faction Scripts written as imaginative or fictitious pieces but purporting to be based upon historic facts and embellished by great attention to documentary detail.

fade down and up (FDU) Traditional way of beginning a VT recording or covering a junction from one programme to another in which the vision mixer fades to black from a studio clock or from the end of an outgoing story and then immediately fades up to the beginning of the incoming story.

fade in The gradual emergence of an image from darkness.

fade out Reverse of **fade in**.

fade out-in (USA) A fade to black and up again to a new image.

fade sound and vision! Studio director's final instruction to the vision mixer and sound supervisor at the close of a recording.

fade to black Complete fade out of an image. The usual end to a television programme.

fade up See **fade in**.

fader Alternative term for **potentiometer (pot)**. Mechanism for fading lights or sound up and down.

falcon mounting A robust location camera mounting with an adjustable jib-arm. Able to carry heavy-weight cameras, it is mounted on tyred wheels for ease of movement.

fall about To collapse in uncontrollable hilarity.

fall off air What happens when a total disaster in the timings or equipment means a programme is incapable of continuing to the end as planned.

family viewing Bland programme deliberately avoiding any controversial content which tries to maximise the audience by offending nobody and appealing to all ages. See **schlock**.

fast film Film stock of greater than usual sensitivity used in low light situations. Most frequently film rated at 400 ISO or more.

fast motion Motion of film through the camera gate at a slower than normal speed resulting in an accelerated effect when the images are projected at normal speed.

father of the chapel (FOC) National Union of Journalists, term for shop steward.

favour To take a shot giving greater prominence to one particular performer than another in a two-shot.

fax System for transmitting facsimiles over a telephone line.

feature film A film made for theatrical release usually of an hour or more in length. See **A feature**, **B feature**, **shorts**.

feature film industry The motion picture industry producing films for commercial cinema distribution.

features Description of documentary or factual programmes dedicated to single topics, as distinct from magazine-type factual programmes.

fee TV (USA) See **toll TV**, **subscription TV**.

feed To transmit a signal by cable or land-lines from one point to another. See **clean feed**.

feed spool Spool from which the film is unwound as it passes through the gate of a camera or projector.

feedback 1. The howling noise resulting from placing a microphone near a speaker which is emitting the amplified signal from the same microphone. See **howl around**. 2. Multiple images achieved by pointing a camera at a monitor carrying the output of the same camera. 3. Response from an audience, either in the form of unsolicited letters, telephone calls, etc or obtained through audience research surveys.

feedback circuit (USA) A **talkback** circuit.

feet per second/frames per second (fps) Two ways of measuring film in television. All film, regardless of gauge, is measured in 35mm feet, i.e. 16 frames to a 35mm foot.

female plug A connecting plug with sockets which receives the projecting pins of a male plug.

Ferrania An Italian film stock manufacturer.

fibre optic Thin optical cable with a lens at one end used for filming inside small models or even the human body.

fiddler's elbow Description of irritating filming condition in which fast-moving clouds cause the light to be continually changing as the sun goes in and out.

field One complete vertical scan of a picture. In a conventional, interlaced picture, two fields are combined to make up each frame or picture.

field banking The period in which the scanning beam of an electronically scanned image returns to the top of the picture. This period is blanked to avoid visible interference on the picture during the flyback.

field frequency The rate of change of fields of picture information (2 fields comprise one complete frame of picture).

field generator (USA) A **colour synthesizer**.

field scan The electronic signal in monitors, cameras, etc, that drives the scanning beam progressively downwards creating the vertical component of the picture and returning the beam rapidly to the top at the end of the picture period.

fight arranger Specialist who is employed to choreograph, and sometimes direct, duels, fights and battles.

figure of eight Microphone which picks up sound in front and behind in a figure of eight pattern, therefore an ideal interview microphone.

fill! 1. Director's instruction to a presenter to busk or improvise for a length of time to cover technical problems. See **fall off air.** 2. General unfocused illumination.

filler A light used to control the depth of shadow, i.e. adjust the contrast ratio of a scene in a standard lighting set-up. See **key light, back light.**

film bin (USA) See **trim bin.**

film break Interruption of a transmission caused by a physical break of the film whilst passing through the projector or telecine machine.

film buff An enthusiast. Someone who memorises the birthdays of actors in old B Feature movies and does not work in the industry. See **semiotics.**

film cement Glue used to join cuts on film. Mostly superseded by tape joins except in negative cutting, but still popular with amateur film makers.

film crew The body of technicians including cameramen, sound recordists, electricians, etc, who work together under the supervision of the director.

film cues See **cue dot.**

film despatch/traffic The offices at all broadcasting centres, laboratories and facility houses which organise the transport of film and sound from one building to another.

film grading The adjustment by a film laboratory of the exposures and colour density in a cutting copy in order to achieve perfect technical uniformity in a show print.

film insert A clip of film dropped into a programme on videotape or live on transmission.

film loop A strip of film joined at both ends to provide endless pictures, generally used for backgrounds such as snow, rain, etc.

film lot A set specially constructed out of doors for filming at a studio to simulate exteriors, e.g. a Western town, a street in a soap opera, etc.

film noir Term used to describe films dealing with crime or corruption whose visual style depends on chiaroscuro lighting and night scenes, e.g. Orson Welles' *A Touch of Evil*, John Houston's *The Asphalt Jungle*.

film operations manager (FOM) Official in a large organisation responsible for allocating film crews and equipment, organising cutting rooms and viewing rushes for technical quality. Also known as **production services manager**.

film ops Film operatives on a film stage, not including the camera crew or the electricians, who are responsible for erecting and moving scenery, props, etc.

film plane Position of the film in relation to the gate of a camera or projector.

film scanner (USA) Telecine machine.

film scanning The process of converting film to electronic signals for transmission or re-recording on videotape.

film speed 1. The speed at which a processed film passes through a projector, e.g. 24 or 25 frames per second. **2.** The measurement of the sensitivity of a film emulsion expressed normally in degrees DIN, ISO or ASA.

film stage An indoor studio for mounting film productions. Also called a **sound stage**.

film stock Unexposed rolls of film.

film strip Compilation of still frames on a single film for projection, normally to support a lecture or presentation.

film unit Synonym for the **film crew**.

filmography Bibliographic listings of the work of technicians and performers compiled by film buffs.

filter Plate of glass or gelatine placed in front of the lens to correct colour or create special effects.

filter factor Scale of values, e.g. 2, 4, 8, given to filters to express how much light a lens filter absorbs and therefore how far the cameraman must compensate by opening the camera aperture.

fine grain print Positive print made with special high-quality, fine-grain **emulsion** for the making of a subsequent good quality negative.

finger trouble Mistakes caused by operator error, particularly in a live studio gallery.

fire brigade (USA) News film unit held in reserve or assigned at short notice to cover unexpected news stories.

fire flicker Rotating filter attachment to a lamp simulating flickering firelight. See also **flicker stick.**

fire lane An area around a studio or a stage which must be kept clear at all times as a fire safety precaution.

fire up Engineering term for switching on cameras and technical equipment and warming it up or otherwise getting it to an operational condition.

fireman Official responsible for fire safety and ensuring that sets and props are fireproof and that all safety procedures are observed.

First Law of Television See **Murphy's law, Second Law of Television.**

first run Theatre/auditorium which habitually shows the premières of feature films before their general distribution.

fish skin Substance gummed on to features to create blemishes, pull back wrinkles, change the shape of eyelids, etc.

fish-eye An extremely wide-angle lens giving a distorted image similar to that seen by a fish from underwater.

fishpole A lightweight portable microphone boom.

five light Soft floodlight with five incandescent bulbs grouped in a single mounting.

five-two-five 525-television line system on the NTSC system used in America and Japan, as distinct from the 625 system, PAL or SECAM used in most of the world.

fixer **1.** Someone paid on a freelance basis who has special local knowledge, e.g. on an overseas trip someone who speaks the language and knows how to handle local officials. **2.** Chemical solution used to complete film processing.

fixing Second bath of chemicals which neutralises the remaining developing solution and chemically fixes the image during film processing.

flag Gesture made by cameraman by waving his hand in front of the lens to indicate to the film editor that he is running continuously without stopping for a board, but that shots before the hand movement may be discarded.

flags Adjustable metal plates mounted in front of a camera or a lamp to suppress spill or flare.

flak Complaints or abuse from the public or politicians poured on controversial programmes.

flame fork A trident-shaped mounting attached to an inflammable gas source used to create the impression of a conflagration when positioned in the foreground of a shot.

flange Metal disk used for winding film on to cores.

flannelgraph Simple visual aid in which cut-out figures with an adhesive backing are pressed to a blackboard covered in flannel. Sometimes used on programmes for children.

flapper A hinged stage flat. See **swinger**.

flare The effect of light reflecting on the surface of the lens itself causing a dazzle on the film or videotape.

flash 1. (noun) News story inserted live into a programme on transmission announcing an unpredicted and sensational event. 2. (verb) to cue a performer by flashing a cue light.

flash box Mechanism with a heater or detonator and magnesium powder or similar which can simulate flashes or explosions on stage. Much used in pantomimes.

flash cut A very short scene of a few frames duration edited in to the main action, usually to suggest a sudden recall of past events or a premonition.

flash fee Copyright payment for the use of a still slide or photographic print.

flash forward Opposite of **flashback**. Normally used to illustrate a premonition.

flash frame Over-exposed or white frames of film either at the beginning of a take before the camera runs up to speed or as a deliberate effect used by a film editor to simulate lightning, explosions, etc.

flash pan (USA) See **whip pan**.

flash pot Remotely detonated pyrotechnic much used in battle sequences and designed to give maximum flash and smoke with minimum casualties amongst the performers.

flashback Scene representing action which has taken place at a time previous to the main action. Usually a brief sequence but may sometimes take up the major part of a film, e.g. *Citizen Kane* by Orson Welles.

flashing 1. The deliberate slight fogging of a film in the laboratory before shooting and processing as a means of increasing the apparent speed of the emulsion. **2.** White random horizontal sparkle on the screen often caused by loss of oxide on videotape, but may also be caused by an electronic fault.

flat A vertical screen used in a stage set to simulate a wall, door, etc.

flat format Standard cine screen projection ratio as distinct from Cinemascope or Panavision. See **academy aperture**.

flat lighting Lighting without prominent key-light, leading to a lack of shadow or depth on a set or a lack of modelling on a face.

flat screen 1. A solid-state display system using micro-chips instead of a cathode-ray tube on a projection screen. **2.** A cathode-ray tube with a flat screen instead of the older versions with a more curved face.

flattage Collective term for two-dimensional uprights simulating walls, doors, etc, in a set. Also called **stage flats**.

flatten To discharge entirely the electrical charge in a battery, often done deliberately prior to recharging.

flesh tones The range of tones in an illuminated human face and thereby the range of tones for whose reproduction electronic equipment has to be adjusted.

flexible collodion See **collodion**.

flicker 1. Patterned, strobing effect on a screen caused by the decoder being unable to distinguish between a close pattern (such as tweed) and subcarrier frequency. 2. A rare combination of picture content that can make the 50 fields/second rate (normally invisible) appear as a visible 25 cycles/second flicker.

flicker stick Pole with strips of cloth attached, which is waved in front of a red lamp to create a firelight effect.

flicks/flickers Early colloquial term for motion pictures and, by extension, the cinema itself.

flies The area above the proscenium from which sets and cloths can be flown up or down.

flip Digital video effect in which an image is made to rotate on its axis vertically or horizontally.

flip/flip-flop Turning over a length of film on an editing machine to reverse the emulsion side making the reverse images.

flip captions/cards Card captions of a standard size mounted on a caption stand with a ring binder.

flip comment Impromptu, irreverent *ad lib* or script line.

flip side The B side of a commercial gramophone record, usually containing a recording thought less likely to be a hit than the track on the A side.

flip-chart Type of teaching aid in the form of an outsize notepad mounted on an easel.

flip-flop 1. Vision mixing panels with two duplicate banks of buttons either of which might be on air depending on the position of a fader. 2. A type of electronic switch. 3. See **flip**.

flipover Wipe effect in which one image is made to reveal another by apparently rotating on its axis, a little like turning the page of a book.

flippers (USA) See **idiot card**.

floater A free-standing flat on castors which can be moved during a production.

flood To light a set overall with soft light.

floor The operational area of a television studio during production. The stage.

floor assistant Assistant to the floor manager during a production, who also assists the director with arrangements during outside rehearsals. In some companies these duties are assumed by an **assistant stage manager**.

floor blocking Rehearsal of performers with the director working on the studio floor instead of from the gallery.

floor lights Lights on stands used in a studio.

floor manager (FM) Operative in charge of the organisation and safety on the floor of an electronic studio during a production, generally in contact with the gallery through earphones.

floor mixer Senior sound recordist on a film stage.

floor monitor Television monitors placed on the studio floor and normally switched to transmission output to keep performers aware of the progress of a programme or for a studio audience.

floor painting The painting of a studio or stage floor with washable paint to simulate a natural surface, e.g. flagstones, floorboards, etc, before the erecting of a set.

floorplan Diagrammatic portrait of the floor area of a studio, marked with a grid pattern on which the positioning of sets and cameras are worked out.

floorstand Television studio lighting stand on a set of castors.

flop-over Reverse the action of a scene from left to right by turning the film over.

flow chart Graphic portrayal of statistics in the form of a graph or similar linear design.

fluff Actor's mistake in speaking.

fluid head A mount for the camera between it and the tripod or dolly enabling it to pan and tilt smoothly. See **Moy camera mount, geared head**.

fluorescent light Light from fluorescent lamps which do not emit the predictable orange hue of tungsten light bulbs and may unpredictably give a scene a blue or green hue on film or tape.

flutter A fault in sound recording caused by mechanical unsteadiness and resulting in a gurgling effect in recorded speech.

fly 1. Digital video effect in which one picture appears to zoom into frame from nothing. 2. To remove part of a set by hoisting it vertically towards the grid.

fly-on-the-wall Documentary filming technique in which the camera crew appears to film real action continuously and without interference, as though eavesdropping.

flyer An irregularity where crew members receiving payment for overnight accommodation choose to return before the scheduled travel time at the end of a shoot.

flying spot A type of telecine machine where the film is pulled past a high-intensity cathode-ray tube and the light passing through the film is focused on to light-sensitive pick-up devices (photocells) which convert the light into red, green and blue electronic signals.

focal length The distance from the optical centre of a lens to the surface of the film. In film terms, it is used to define the angle of view of a lens, e.g. a 5.9mm lens gives a very wide view, a 300mm lens gives a very narrow telephoto angle of view.

focal plane The flat surface parallel with the plane of the lens which is at the focal point of the lens.

focus puller An assistant to the camera operator who is responsible for operating the focus control on a lens during a complex camera movement.

focus ring Ring control around a lens by which the cameraman adjusts focus.

focus track Lightweight plastic rails for a camera dolly.

focus up! Director's instruction to an electronic cameraman to check the focus on the part of the scene required.

fog filter A filter used to diffuse light, creating a soft focus or misty effect.

fog machine/maker See **smoke gun**.

fogging Result of unwanted light getting into a film resulting in a dull, foggy effect on the processed film. Film is sometimes deliberately fogged before proper exposure for special effects.

foldback Sound external to the studio itself played back from the gallery through speakers on the studio floor, e.g. for pop musicians to mime to.

follow focus Adjustment of the focus on a lens during an action in which either the performer moves back or forward or the camera is moving in order to keep the main subject in sharp focus. Done by the focus puller.

follow focus cameraman (USA) Dolly shot.

follow spot A manœuvrable spotlight with an intense narrow beam on a fixed mounting which may be panned and tilted by an operator to follow an artist. Used in light entertainment programmes and on the theatre stage.

follow-up News item which is based on a previously broadcast item.

foot candles A scale to express the intensity of incident light shown on a scene. See **foot lambert**.

foot lambert The standard measurement of incident light replacing the now defunct foot candle.

footage Measurement of film. A 35mm foot contains 16 frames. Confusingly, dubbing theatres and editors use 35mm foot as a measurement when working with 16mm film, e.g. a 16mm foot = 16 frames although a real measured foot of 16mm film has 40 frames.

footage counter Attachment to editing desk or in a dubbing theatre to measure the number of film feet which have passed through the **gate**.

footlights Theatrical term for ground row lights placed extreme down-stage facing the performance.

footprint The geographical area beneath the communications satellite in which the transmitted signal can be received.

forced processing Laboratory technique for developing film at a higher temperature than normal, effectively to increase the speed of under-exposed film.

foreground Part of a scene or composition nearest to the camera.

foreground matte A monochrome picture used to generate a signal that enables an electronic switch to inhibit an overlay, e.g. part of a background can be re-inserted into the picture so that an artist appears as part of a scene rather than in front of it.

foreground music Music which appears to emanate naturally from the scene or action, e.g. a gramophone, radio, orchestra in vision, etc. Opposite of **background music**.

foreground piece Scenery or property placed in the foreground of a shot to increase the impression of depth. See **dingle shot**.

foreign desk Section of newsroom responsible for international coverage.

foreign release Version of a film specially modified for distribution outside the country of origin.

foreigner A filming trip overseas.

format 1. The shape of a film as projected, i.e. wide screen or flat format. **2.** The overall look or style of a programme, particularly in terms of programmes in a series.

formula film/show Film or programme following a thoroughly predictable sequence of events enacted by two-dimensional characters which makes few demands upon the audience's attention, but often enjoys high ratings.

forty-second burst (FSB) (radio) A 40" voice piece which sits on a 40" cartridge.

four-o-five (405) lines Obsolete television line standard used before the advent of colour.

four plate A Steenbeck-type editing table with two plates for the film picture and two plates for the film sound, i.e. which can only play a single sound track at one time. See **editing machine/bench**.

four walling Cinema distribution rental system in which a distributor rents a theatre on a fixed weekly basis as opposed to splitting the profits of the box office with the owner.

frame A single picture on a length of film or VT. In Britain there are traditionally 25 frames

per second in TV. Feature films use 24 frames
per second.

frame bar (USA) See **frame line**.

frame counter Device attached to a camera
registering the amount of film which has been
exposed in numbers of frames.

frame hold 1. Obvious by its absence as when
a film jumps in the gate of a projector or a VT
machine fails to hold the image steady in its
intended frame. **2.** A monitor/television set
adjustment to hold the picture vertically steady
on the screen. See **frame slip**.

frame jog The ability to freeze single frames of
videotape during editing.

frame jump (USA) See **crossing the line**.

frame line The narrow line of unexposed film
between frames or the line between frames of
videotape.

frame roll 1. A monitor/television set losing
vertical hold. **2.** Loss of synchronisation of
equipment driven by pulses from the master
pulse generator, causing the picture to move up
or down. **3.** A single movement of the frame bar
up the screen on a cut to a new picture so that the
new picture is revealed by the movement of the
frame bar. Resembles a vertical wipe but is
caused by the pictures not being synchronous,
i.e. the pulses creating the pictures are not
exactly together so that there is a pulse disturbance on the cut confusing receivers and monitors.

frame slip Effect seen on TV screens when,
due to loss of synchronisation, the bars become
visible and appear as lines rolling across the
pictures and the picture itself jumps. Obvious
also as an effect when a film camera is pointed at
a TV screen and the two sets of images are not
synchronous. See **roll bar**.

frame store Electronic means of holding an individual frame of a moving television picture.

frame stretch Slowing down the action by repeating each successive frame two or more times by step printing in a laboratory. Effectively, the way of achieving a slow motion effect on videotape.

framing Composing a shot within the confines of the sides of the viewfinder frame. A scene may so be described by parts which are composed 'in the frame' and those which are excluded by the camera 'out of frame'.

franchise system System of granting monopoly franchises to commercial television companies in the British Isles on a regional basis by the Independent Broadcasting Association.

free cinema Originally a description of British documentary films made by directors to make personal comment and later used to describe a school of socially or politically committed directors in feature films during the 1960's.

freebie Trip or function paid for by someone unconnected with the production. See **facility trip, swan**.

freelance Someone who is self-employed and who contracts to work on programmes on an *ad hoc* basis.

freeze 1. To become utterly immobile on stage, either for dramatic effect or as a result of forgetting the next action cue in a moment of panic or amnesia. **2.** To arrest action by holding a single frame of film or videotape for a length of time.

freeze frame Abrupt freezing of a frame of film or tape to make it appear as a still photograph.

French brace Triangular folding frame fitted to the back of a piece of scenery.

French flag A metal plate mounted on the

front of a camera lens like a windscreen visor in a motor car to cut off glare from lamps.

frequency The rate of change of a signal that alternates in direction at regular intervals, measured in Hertz (replacing the more descriptive term of cycles per second).

frequency modulation (FM) Modulation of a high-frequency carrier wave where the frequency of the carrier varies in step with a lower frequency modulating signal, e.g. audio or video.

fresnel lens Lens constructed of concentric circles which controls the beam angle. Used in lighthouses and stage spotlights, because less liable to heat fracture than a conventional lens.

friction head A panning and tilting mechanism between a camera and a tripod with an adjustable sliding friction plate which facilitates slow but steady movements.

fringing The appearance of a halo of incorrect colour at the margins of colour areas causing blurring of the image.

frocks Familiar term for costumes or, collectively, for the wardrobe department.

from the top From the very beginning of a script or a scene.

front leader Film manufactured with printed countdown in seconds or feet put at the beginning of a roll of film for transmission or projection.

front man A presenter who appears in vision on a magazine-type show and who links recorded inserts or conducts interviews.

front out Film which has been rewound correctly so that the front leader is at the beginning. Opposite of **end-out/tail out**. Also called **head out**.

front porch Black level signal following the

synchronising pulse and preceding the active
television line.

front projection Still or moving scene
projected on the front of a screen. See **axial
front projection**.

frontboard A clapperboard at the beginning of
any take to give the film editor an identification
and a point to synchronise the sound and pictures.

frying Sizzling noise on a microphone caused
by faulty plug or amplifier or interference on a
radio mike.

fuff Light plastic foam used to simulate snow.

Fuji A Japanese manufacturer of film stock.

full flood When an adjustable lamp is at its
widest beam or most de-focused condition.

full frame 1. Composing a shot to include the
desired object or person, but close enough to
exclude as much as possible of anything else.
2. Exposure of the complete maximum frame
size of a gauge of film as distinct from half
frame.

full shot/FS (USA) See **long shot**.

full track Reference to a magnetic sound
recording using the whole width of the tape
(many tape recorders employ only half a track at
a time).

fuller's earth Dried clay powder sometimes
used by designers to simulate dust.

fully practical A property or part of a set
which is real and functioning, e.g. a kitchen
appliance, a gun which will be fired. Often
abbreviated to **fully prac**.

fulmar A type of pedestal studio camera
mounting.

futures meeting Regular editorial meeting held
by newsroom staff to discuss the coverage of
forthcoming stories in the news diary.

G AZE See **ganged Angenieux zoom equipment.**

GPI See **general porte instruction.**

GV Script abbreviation for **general view.**

gadabout Film camera dolly mounted on a motor car suspension system.

gaffer Chief electrician where a team of electricians is employed.

gaffer grips/clamp A pair of sprung calipers for gripping projections, pipes, etc, from which lightweight luminaires may be supported.

gaffer tape Strong, wide, adhesive tape used by electricians and practically everyone else in studio or on location.

gag/wind gag Blimp or other attachment to a microphone to cut out the noise of wind or rain on the mike-head.

gagman (USA) A writer specialising in writing and visualising jokes or brief sketches for artists or programmes.

gain Increase in signal power, usually expressed in decibels.

gain control 1. Control on an electronic camera which increases or decreases its light sensitivity abilities. 2. Electronic amplification of video or audio signals.

gallery The part of an electronic studio which houses the director, vision mixer, production assistant and certain of the engineers. Also known as production control room and, in USA, as **control.**

gallows arm Triangular gibbet-shaped extension to a set which can be used to hang drapes which disguise shooting off.

galvanometer A meter for measuring voltages.

gamma A measure of the transfer characteristic

(relationship between input and output) of a film or electronic pickup or television signal chain, where output = input raised to the power of gamma.

gamma correction A deliberate distortion of a video signal that amplifies the darker tones in the picture more than the lighter tones. Used to correct for the opposite characteristic of a cathode-ray tube to give an correct overall tonal reproduction.

ganged Locked together so that movement of one causes identical movement in the other(s).

ganged Angenieux zoom equipment (GAZE) System for coupling together the zooms on two different cameras, sometimes used in shows dependent on use of complex chromakey/colour separation overlay effects.

gantry The walkway around the upper part of the studio wall giving access to the **lighting rig**.

gardening Cutting out intrusive branches of greenery or placing the same in the foreground of a shot to improve the composition. The bane of park-keepers. See **dingle shot**.

GARDENING

gas pedestal Studio camera pedestal in which the weight of the camera is taken by a column of compressed air.

gash print Print of archive material on to a cutting copy for working or dubbing purposes. The rough print is taken direct from the positive.

gate The mechanism in a camera or projector which holds the film whilst the shutter exposes or projects the frame.

gauge Width of film stock, normally 8mm, 16mm and 35mm.

gauze Panel of cloth which appears as a solid part of the set when front lit, but which becomes transparent when back lit.

gauze shot Shot of a painted gauze or translucent backdrop which, lit from the front, is opaque but transparent when lit from the back.

geared head Mechanism on a camera mounting which is operated by a mechanical system of gears and handles for controlling complex camera movements.

gel Gelatine or plastic sheeting used to change the colour of light emitted by lamps. See **Cinemoid**.

general porte instruction (GPI) Command system on all sophisticated edit controllers. Command instruction to start all audio systems, CDs, DVE.

general release Widespread distribution of a feature film instead of, or after, showing in selected first release theatres.

general view (GV) A very wide, establishing shot.

generation Describes the number of times in the editing process that the original videotape has to be copied, e.g. the original tape is first generation, but the first copy is a second, and a re-edit may involve copying on to a third.

generator Equipment for generating electricity for lights. Often used inaccurately as a term for an alternator.

genlock The automatic correction of a local pulse generator so that its pulses are locked precisely to a remote pulse generator.

gennie Abbreviation for **generator**.

genre film Up-market description of films or programmes made to a recognisable or predictable formula, e.g. Western, suburban sitcom, cops and robbers.

geography shot An establishing shot used at the beginning of a scene or interview to establish the location of subsequent action. See **general view**.

geometric distortion Non-linear scanning of camera monitors and receivers that results in distortion of the original scene.

geometry The relationship of film frames to the sprocket holes, e.g. 16mm, super 16 single perf., double perf., etc.

geostationary satellite A satellite in an orbit that keeps it in the same position relative to earth.

geosynchronous satellite Satellite whose orbit takes the same time as one rotation of the earth.

gerb Type of pyrotechnic used to create showers of sparks.

ghetto blaster A large, portable sound cassette recorder/player with two built-in recorders and twin loudspeakers frequently seen pressed to the ears of young persons with hearing disorders.

ghoster Film term for claiming an overnight whilst in fact travelling home after a shoot. In television. See **flyer**.

ghosting Repetition of an image caused by

reflection of signal and common on domestic receivers with ill-positioned aerials.

gi-go, Garbage in, garbage out. Term applied to computer-controlled processes.

gig Performance or recording session by a musical group.

gimmick Unusual trick or artifice used to grab the attention of an audience. See **breathe on, treatment, angle**.

giraffe (USA) See **lazy arm**.

gizmo Description of any piece of tricky equipment with no other common name, e.g. an electronic box to synchronise a film camera with a TV receiver.

glass matte Trick-shot in which the live action appears against a background glass painting.

glass shot Shot taken through a sheet of glass or clear plastic on which part of the scene has been painted in by an artist.

glaze Gloss surface on a photographic positive.

glitch White flashes or sparkle on pictures generally caused by tape drop-out or electrical interference.

glitch check A check on the quality of a videotape by a machine that counts the **drop-outs**.

glitter 1. Sparkling particles physically thrown or dropped into a scene. See **Disney dust**. 2. A flash on the picture momentarily overloading the pick-up device, generally caused by reflections from bright objects such as jewellery.

go! Direction used by gallery director to cue sound, e.g. *go grams!* or *go tape!* Used instead of the word **run** which is used for pictures, e.g. *run VT!* or *run TK!*.

go down Failure of an item of electrical equipment.

go grams! Command used in studio to play in discs or tape recordings.

go-between Origin of word **gobo** — a cutout foreground device for lights.

gobo Adjustable metal frame in front of a lamp to restrict the beam and project a cut-out pattern on the cyclorama or set.

God slot Part of a programme schedule regularly devoted to religious broadcasting.

gods Highest balcony of seats in a theatre.

gofer Do-er of odd jobs or runner on location. Often someone with an impressive-sounding title. From '*go for this, go for that*'.

golden oldie Recording or programme from the past, long forgotten, often with good reason, but revived with the intention of evoking nostalgia without costing too much money.

golden section Guide to picture composition in which the screen is divided into nine equal rectangles. The optimum points of interest will be located along the horizontal lines towards the points of intersection with the vertical lines.

golden time Term used by technicians in ITV companies to describe overtime hours where payment goes beyond double time to the maximum hourly rate applicable.

goldfishing The consequence of trying to edit dialogue on commag film where sound and picture are synchronous in effect but not physically alongside each other on the film. A sound and picture cut results in several frames of mouths opening and shutting before the first sound comes in.

goody Newsroom term of approval for an exciting subject or item.

Governors A body of independent people appointed by the government as guardians of the standards and independence of the BBC as defined by its Charter.

gradation The range of densities in an image from highlights to shadows.

graded broadcast Programme regarded as of national importance, so given priority and special facilities for duplicating technical back-up.

graded print A film print corrected in the printing process to achieve optimum quality.

grading **1.** Film printing or electronic method of equalising the differences in colour balance and contrast in different shots which have been cut together in a scene. **2.** The process in a film laboratory where a colour grader corrects the colour balance and exposure of the different shots in a film negative to achieve a homogeneous-looking print.

graduated filter Neutral density filter which is darker at the top or bottom to correct a scene of extreme contrast, e.g. a graduated filter darker at the top half may be used to darken a skyline to give a stormy impression.

grain The small particles of oxidised material on film which make up the image after exposure. The faster the film the longer the size of grain, which becomes apparent to the eye giving a graining effect. Video cameras operating in low light give similar-looking effects where it is known as **noise**.

Grampian Television Commercial television contractor for the north of Scotland.

grams General term for gramophone records, but also collectively the department in the BBC responsible for record and tape libraries as well as the playback machines and personnel to work them.

grams deck Turntable with pick-up arm.

grams swinger An assistant to a dubbing mixer or sound supervisor in a studio who cues and plays in discs and tapes.

Granada Television Commercial television company with the IBA franchise for the English north-western counties.

Granadaland Fictitious region of northern Britain where working-class social realism is identified as the dominant programme style.

graphic equaliser A device that can vary the frequency response of a sound replay system over the entire audio spectrum. A do-it-yourself sound balancing console in domestic hi-fi equipment.

graphics Artwork applied to television, ranging from simple news captions to complex animation sequences.

graphics artist An artist who is responsible overall for name captions, glass shots, computer-generated graphics, opening titles, etc.

Grass Valley A manufacturer of electronic vision mixing and special effects equipment.

grazing props See **extra**.

green card 1. Air travel credit card much used by crews to cover excess baggage requirements in flying their equipment around the globe. **2.** United States work permit.

green film Film print straight from the laboratory bath and still damp.

green print (USA) A show print fresh from the laboratories and not yet run through a projector.

green room Traditionally the room in a theatre used by actors as a rest or common room. In TV stations often the room where guests wait before going on air and where hospitality is served.

gremlin Invisible and unidentifiable cause of catastrophic equipment failure commonly

grey scale

GREMLIN

attributed by engineers to finger trouble by others.

grey scale A graduated scale of tones from white through shades of grey to black used to align technical equipment and as a standard for grading black and white film.

grid 1. Electronically-generated geometric pattern which a studio cameraman can super-impose over his shot to check its alignment.
2. Suspended framework under the ceiling of a studio giving access to lighting and scenery hoists.

grille An electronic signal used by engineers to line up pictures, comprising a grid pattern of white lines on a black background or vice versa.

grip Person in charge of operating mobile camera mountings, dollies, cranes, etc, so called because in the early cinema the job was given to the man who carried the director's suitcase on location. (USA) grips.

ground row Lights in groups of two or four which may be driven from separate dimmers and separately coloured, if desired, designed to illuminate a backing or cyclorama from the ground.

group faders Faders for controlling banks of lights or microphones together.

group shot A shot, usually a long shot, that includes a number of people.

groupie Female follower of a rock group or, more generally, any hanger-on or obsessive admirer.

guessing stick Cameraman's term for an exposure meter.

guest star/appearance A supporting role written into a soap opera or series in which a well-known performer appears briefly in the hope of boosting the interest of the audience.

guide track Sound track recorded while filming dance to playback. Used by the editor to match action to the relevant passage of music or the clean master track.

gully pedestal Location camera mounting for large video cameras.

gun See **electron gun**.

gun mike A highly directional microphone hand-held or attached to a boom — much used on television.

gyro error Error introduced to a portable video recording by movement of the machine.

gyro head A camera head designed to hold a camera steady in adverse conditions, e.g. a helicopter.

gyro zoom Zoom lens gyroscopically stabilised for shooting from moving vehicles, etc.

gyrosphere Gyroscopically-controlled camera mounting specially designed for helicopters and fast-moving ground vehicles.

H/A Abbreviation for **high angle**.

HDTV See **high definition TV**.

HMI Abbreviation for **hydragyrum medium iodide**. A discharge lamp with a colour temperature similar to daylight.

HT See **high tension**.

HTV See **Harlech Television**.

hack See **journalist**.

hair/hair in the gate A piece of film or film emulsion which becomes detached and then jammed in the gate of a camera or a projector giving the impression of a hair or a piece of fluff stuck on the front of the lens.

hair dryer Used on location to dry out a portable video recorder for damp.

hair piece A wig.

hairwork (USA) Wigs or postiche.

halation Brilliant reflected light on the film emulsion appearing as spots or tracks of illumination.

half frame A format of 35mm film which, by using only half an individual frame, achieves a wide-screen image without the use of an anamorphic lens and with consequent saving of film stock.

half tones Middle tones in an image between shadows and highlights.

half track Sound recording in which the magnetic track occupies only one half of the tape.

halide Light-sensitive metal compound used for a film emulsion.

hall of mirrors Digital video effect in which an image appears to be reflected in an infinitely receding series of mirror images.

halo Generally a camera lens flare caused by an excessively low back light.

halogen A range of gases used in some light bulbs to emit a brilliant light; typically iodine, fluorine, etc.

ham 1. An amateur radio or TV operator. **2.** A wildly over-emphatic actor. See **over the top**.

ham it up Deliberate over-playing of a part by a performer.

hammocking The deliberate placing of a weak programme between two highly popular ones in order to boost its audience figures. See **pre-echo, inheritance factor**.

hand basher Hand-held location battery lamp.

hand camera Small camera designed for use without a tripod .

hand carried Film equipment taken to location by air as cabin baggage, rather than by freight.

hand crank Early movie technique of winding the film through the camera by a manually-operated handle.

hand cue See **hand signals**.

hand flag Cameraman signal for the picture editor made by waving a hand in front of the lens to indicate that a take is no good and that it will be repeated immediately.

hand mike A stick microphone, much used by pop singers, and in television news used widely by reporters. See **wand**.

hand props See **action props**.

hand signals Signals given by the floor manager to presenters, artists, etc, to cue action, wind up a discussion, etc, which can be done silently in the presenter's or artist's eyeline.

hand-held When the cameraman removes the camera from the tripod and operates it from the shoulder for greater ease of movement in an unpredictable situation, or to achieve a special effect.

handback Closing words from a contributor on a distant location to the anchorman of a topical programme signalling the end of that item.

handler Person designated to be responsible for animals appearing in a production.

handout Free publicity material provided by an organisation to journalists by public relations officers in the well-founded hope that it will be used or included in what passes for original copy.

handover Term used in a two-handed news or magazine programme in which the presenters alternate and one makes reference to the other at a change of item.

hands off 1. A location camera operated in its automatic exposure mode. 2. Equipment line-up or adjustments that are carried out automatically by sensors within the equipment, without or with very limited human intervention.

hands on Training techniques in which learning takes place by actually doing a task rather than receiving classroom instruction.

hanging bars Parts of the studio grid from which scenery may be flown.

hanging irons Metal bracket screwed to top of scenery to enable it to be flown from the hanging bars.

hard copy Term used in an electronic news-room to describe a printed copy of a script as opposed to the words typed directly on a VDU.

hard core Programmes with little, but an overtly pornographic, content. See **soft core, family viewing**.

hard focus Image in which the focus is so sharp that outlines appear hard-edged.

hard light Focused light source giving a sharp, well-defined shadow of the illuminated subject. See **key light**.

hard news Straight, serious reporting of an important event without background embellishment or interpretative analysis.

hard sell Commercial technique where a presenter addresses the audience direct and tells them what to think and buy. See **soft sell**.

hard story A story with obvious, immediate political or social content.

hard wire Connection of two pieces of equipment or technical areas through fixed, ducted cables and plugs.

Harlech Television (HTV) British commercial TVcompany for Wales and the west of England.

harmonic generator Sound device used for producing harmonics of fundamental frequency for special sound effects.

Harriet A simplified version of Harry.

Harry Video digital effects system made by Quantel.

harsh Lighting technique using hard light from one predominant direction, generally producing an unflattering portrait.

Haute Autorité French governing body with overall responsibility for all television and radio networks.

hazard tape Wide adhesive tape marked with broad, brightly-coloured stripes for marking cables, ill-lit obstacles on a studio floor, etc.

haze filter (USA) See **fog filter**.

head 1. A pan and tilt mechanism mounted between the camera and the tripod. 2. The part of a videotape machine which is in contact with the tape and actually records or plays back the signal on the tape. 3. Main body of a camera, excluding the lens and magazines.

head clog Fault which occurs when dirt or pieces of detached magnetic tape become jammed in a recording or playback head or a videotape machine.

head leader Film at the start of a film with numbers to allow synchronisation prior to projection.

head on tail away (USA) Transition in which a character approaches the camera until either going out of focus or blocking the lens completely, subsequently cutting to another black frame or unfocused shot from which the same or another character moves into focus.

head out Film wound on a spool so that the front of the film is outermost.

head title (USA) Identification name caption at the top of a frame as opposed to the more usual position in the lower third.

header Crossbeam above head height on a set forming a lintel over an opening.

headlamp/headlight A spotlight mounted directly on top of a camera.

headline sequence Montage of shots at the top of a news or magazine programme trailing the subsequent main stories.

headphones Earphones.

headroom Area between top of the head and the upper edge of the screen in a close up shot .

headset Headphones with a microphone attached, particularly used on outside broadcasts.

hear back (USA) To listen to the replay of a recording.

hearing aid See **deaf aid**.

heavy 1. A dramatic role in which the character is identified as a villain or muscle man. **2.** An actor who specialises in such roles. **3.** A **hard news** story.

Heli-Tele Commercial agency handling helicopter photography.

helical scan The means of ensuring that the moving video head or heads in a video recorder describe long diagonal tracks along the tape by wrapping the tape in the form of one turn of a helix around a drum carrying the video head or heads.

herogram Enthusiastic congratulations for a newsman somewhere unpleasant from editorial colleagues who are glad that they are not with him.

heron Studio camera crane with a jib and motorised dolly.

herringbone pattern A fault condition on a quadruplex VTR that causes verticals to zig-zag down the picture.

Hertz (Hz) Modern term for cycles per second of an alternating signal.

Hertzian waves The radiated signal from a transmitter.

hessian A textured cloth frequently used as a backing in a studio.

hexiplex A device which allows up to six VTR's to be switched down one line to a studio.

hi-fi General, popular term for high-fidelity stereo sound equipment.

hidden camera A camera concealed from an audience or unwitting participants in a pro- gramme, e.g. **candid camera**.

hide Construction to conceal a film cameraman whilst filming wildlife.

Hi-8 Videotape format, once purely amateur, but increasingly profession, using video approximate to 8mm film or standard audio cassettes.

high angle shot A shot taken with the lens height above the action or the eyeline of the performer.

high band U-matic three-quarter-inch videotape format used for broadcast quality material on the European 625-line system.

high band SP Better quality, more sophisticated version of above.

high definition television (HDTV) Generic term to cover a number of competing systems offering improved pictures when compared with 525/625-line systems. The principal systems use 16 x 9 aspect ratio and 1250 lines/50 fields (Europe), 1050 lines/60 fields (USA) or 1125 lines/60 fields (Japan).

high fidelity Any good quality pictures or sound.

high frequency **1.** (radio) An alternative signal in the range 3MHz to 30 Hz, approximately the short wave radio band. **2.** (sound) The upper end of the audio range, approximately 5kHz to 20kHz.

high hat Camera mounting enabling the camera to be positioned a few inches from the ground.

high intensity Sometimes used to imply a discharge light source such as an HMI giving a bright white light.

high key (USA) A term indicating a cheerful mood, associated with light entertainment and comedy, where the tones are light in colour and texture.

high key lighting Lighting where there is high luminance and low colour saturation, e.g. simulating normal bright daylight. Generally, employs a relatively low ratio of hard to soft light, e.g. 1 1/2:1.

high pass filter Sound equipment for removing unwanted low frequencies from a recording.

high shot See **high angle shot**.

high speed camera A film camera designed to be run very fast so that the film when subsequently replayed at normal speed shows the action in slow motion.

high speed film Film rated normally at 400 ISO or over, which is ultra sensitive and allows filming in extremely low light set-ups.

high speed filming Filming with the film passing the gate at a speed faster than the standard 24/25 frame per second which, on projection, results in a slow-motion effect. Also called **overcranking**.

high tension (HT) The DC voltages required to make electronic circuits function. May be anything from a few volts to several hundred volts.

highlight 1. A high specular reflection often emphasised by star filters. 2. Any area of extreme brilliance on a scene.

Hilversum A small town near Amsterdam, originally the transmission site for Dutch radio, now the centre for almost all Dutch television production companies, recording studios, etc.

hit 1. A popular song or act which wins great passing acclaim. 2. A commercial success. 3. (USA) Instruction to activate a piece of equipment by pressing a button, e.g. hit sound.

hit parade Old term for lists of commercially successful popular recordings. See **charts**.

hit the mark For an actor to arrive at a carefully rehearsed position in a scene or to place a property on its correct spot for the camera.

hog To try to monopolise a microphone or camera during a live programme. See **upstage**.

hoist 1. Mechanism for flying studio or stage scenery and lights. 2. Various kinds of crane for cameras, e.g. cherry picker, Simon hoist.

hold a shot To keep a camera frame or movement until a clear instruction from the director to cut.

hold it! 1. Director's instruction to stop a rehearsal or recording. **2.** (OB) Director's instruction to a cameraman to stop a zoom or hold the frame.

hold-frame Benchwork animation term for **a freeze frame**.

Hollywood Suburb of Los Angeles containing feature film studios and now also a major television production centre.

holograph A laser projection device that can produce three-dimensional images.

Home Box Office (USA) Cable TV channel specialising in feature films.

home desk Section of newsroom concerned with national and local stories.

home movies Amateur film shot usually on 8mm.

honey wagon Mobile lavatory used on location shoots.

hoofer A dancer.

hook 1. A title sequence or headline sequence signposting the main contents of a programme in order to persuade the viewers to stay with it. **2.** Distortion of a TV signal causing the vertical lines to appear to hook over at the top of frame.

horizontal hold The relationship between the horizontal scanning rate of a receiver or monitor and the received video signals horizontal pulses.

horror film Genre of Gothic production in which supernatural forces terrorise the principal characters and, it is hoped, the viewers.

horse A crossbeam mounted over a bin on which film trims can be clipped or pinned.

horse opera Hollywood term for a Western film. Also called an **oater**.

HORROR FILM

hosepiping Careless hand-held camerawork resulting in endless panning and zooming shots.

hosted 1. Show presented by a celebrity who introduces personalities or stars to an invited audience. See **invited guest**. **2.** BBC term for a show produced in one region but recorded by another.

hot Electrically live equipment.

hot camera An electronic camera in standby, i.e. with some circuits switched off to conserve power, but able to produce instant pictures at the flick of a switch.

hot cutting (USA) Cutting non-synchronous pictures on a vision mixing desk. See **panic button**.

hot head Remotely operated pan and tilt head used on large camera cranes.

hot line Exclusive control line on a production, e.g. between a studio telephone or performer on a deaf aid and a producer or editor in the gallery.

hot pod A tripod with an easily-elevated central column, useful for ENG work.

hot press Machine for printing coloured foil name captions on to card, now largely replaced by electronically generated letters.

hot splice A film join made by using film cement instead of splicing tape.

hot spot Part of a set or an image greatly over-lit in relation to the rest.

hot switch To switch between two programme sources, e.g. an outside broadcast and a regional magazine show, live on air.

house lights Normal working lights in a studio or in a theatre auditorium.

housing A sealed camera blimp used for underwater filming.

howl around 1. Problem which arises where a microphone is left open near to a speaker playing back its own input, normally resulting in a high-pitched howl. 2. Where a studio camera is deliberately pointed at a monitor, showing the same camera's output leading to an effect like looking at an infinite number of mirrors reflecting each other.

hum Unwanted, continuous, low-frequency interference from the mains on electronic equipment. May be caused by a fault or a heavy mains current passing near a sensitive electronic circuit.

hum bars Interference from the mains causing horizontal bars to run up or down the picture.

human interest story Story in which ordinary people are shown in situations of great pathos. Paradoxically, human interest stories are most frequently about animals.

hunt 1. Function of an automatically-controlled transmitter which, in case of a total breakdown, searches for the strongest available alternative signal. **2.** Instruction to an OB or studio cameraman in an unrehearsed situation to look for suitable shots to offer the director and vision mixer.

hunter Telephone system which will transfer incoming calls to an engaged number to another extension not in use.

hybrid system Devices that employ a combination of apparently different techniques, ostensibly to exploit the advantages of both, e.g. a programme shot on video but using a slash film print to enable sound dubbing in a film dubbing theatre or a transmission system using a combination of analogue and digital signals.

hydraulic system Motorised device driven by liquid pressure, e.g. oil, water, etc.

hymn sheet Running order or studio script.

hype Artificially to puff a programme, recording or artist by excessive publicity prior to public showing.

hyper-cardioid mike See **gun mike**.

hypo Chemical photographic processing agent, usually sodium thiosulphate.

IBA See **Independent Broadcasting Authority**.

IBC See **International Broadcasting Convention**.

IMTF See **Independent Media Training Federation**.

Int. Script abbreviation for **interior** scene.

IPPA See **Independent Programme Producers Association**.

ips See **inches per second**.

ISO See **International Standardisation Organisation**.

ITA See **Independent Television Authority**.

ITCA See **Independent Television Companies Association**.

ITN See **Independent Television News**.

ITS See **insertion test signals**.

I/V See abbreviation for **in vision**.

IVAC See **International Video & Audio Convention**.

iceblock Prism assembly in a colour camera.

iconoscope Type of early camera tube.

ident The pictorial and/or sound identification of a film or recording at its beginning.

ident board A board on which the relevant information about a programme may be written, e.g programme title, shot number, etc. Sometimes, in a studio, combined with a count-down clock.

idiot board/card A large card with the text of a script written in large letters and held up by a camera for presenters or actors who cannot remember their lines.

idiot's lantern A domestic TV receiver.

Ikegami Japanese camera manufacturer of video cameras, often abbreviated to **Ikky**.

image A picture as focused on to the film,

pick-up device or displayed on a cathode-ray tube.

image conforming A process where film negatives are transferred to a videotape format and all editing is carried out on tape.

image diagonal The measurement between the opposite diagonal corners of the image on the face of a TV screen. The size of a commercial TV receiver is expressed by image diagonal, e.g. 30-inch screen.

image enhancement Electronic sharpening of a TV picture.

image intensifier Attachment used particularly for night shooting enabling a cameraman to see and film in very dark conditions. Derived from military night-sights for guns.

image orthicon An early camera tube that employed a target either three or four-and-a-half inches in diameter and photo-multipliers to amplify the signal.

image trail Video digital effect created by building up a composite of freeze frames trailing each other.

image transfer Transfer of film to videotape or vice versa.

imaginary line See **crossing the line, line of action/axis**.

Imax A very large screen, 70mm film projection system.

impedance Combined effect of resistance and reactance to the flow of current in an AC circuit.

improvisation Spontaneous unscripted dialogue by actors either as an *ad lib* during a programme or as a contribution towards a final script during rehearsal.

in shot Within the frame of a cameraman's picture.

in sync **1.** Picture and sound perfectly synchronised. **2.** Pulses from different sources synchronised.

in the can A satisfactorily completed programme or scene.

in vision (I/V) Within the frame of the camera picture. In news, specifically refers to a journalist appearing to deliver a piece directly to the viewers.

in-betweener Junior animation artist who draws the cels in a cartoon to link the main frames of significant action drawn by the master animator.

in-camera editing Shooting shots in sequence to avoid subsequent editing, a technique used by experimental film makers and amateurs.

in-filling Term used by programme planners to describe the filling up of programme slots during the day to achieve 24-hours television.

incandescence The ability of certain elements to give out light when heated to a high temperature.

inches per second (ips) The measure of the running speed of magnetic recording tape.

inching Act of carefully moving film back or forth in a camera or projector gate frame-by-frame.

incident light The measurement of the light which falls on a scene or object as opposed to the light which is reflected from it.

incidental music Mood music played underneath dialogue or commentary.

incline prism Silvered prism placed in front of lens for very high or low-angle filming.

Incorporated Society of Musicians Professional association representing concert artists and conductors.

indemnity Insurance against loss, injury or damage taken out by a production in relation to particular locations or activities.

Independent Broadcasting Authority (IBA) Statutory supervisory body for British commercial radio and television companies responsible for allocating regional broadcasting franchises.

Independent Media Training Federation Training body for the independent and freelance sector of the film and televison industry.

Independent Programme Producers Association (IPPA) Association of independent programme makers representing companies operating outside the major broadcast television companies, although often contributing to them.

Independent Television (ITV) Erroneous, popular term used to describe the British commercial television companies.

Independent Television Authority (ITA) The regulatory body for the British Independent TV companies expanded to include radio and re-named **Independent Broadcasting Authority** (q.v.).

Independent Television Companies Association (ITCA) Joint association representing the interests of the franchise holding companies of British Commercial Television.

Independent Television News (ITN) Independent body providing national and international news for the British commercial television companies.

independents/indies Production companies outside the main BBC/IBA structure who produce programmes in collaboration with broadcast transmission companies.

industrial camera A camera occupying the

middle ground between the amateur home video market and the demanding technical standards of the broadcast engineers. Usually used for closed circuit television.

industrial films/TV Programmes sponsored by industrial organisations for close circuit use within their companies or for the promotion of their products.

infinity The distance from a camera lens at which all objects in view will be in sharp focus.

infinity cyclorama A curved cyclorama which, suitably lit and with a matching painted floor, gives a background showing no joins and implying infinity or limbo. Best achieved by a moat to accommodate both bottom of cyclorama and ground row lights.

inflexible collodion See **collodion**.

informational film Film with an explicit educational or industrial message.

infotainment Portmanteau word, information + entertainment. Style of programme-making in which news and other factual programmes are glamorized. In the USA, covers such practices as reconstruction of violent crime to titillate the viewers.

infra-red filming Photography using special film sensitive to heat which makes it possible to get pictures in otherwise totally dark conditions, e.g. of animals.

ingénue Young leading role. The age at which an actress becomes disqualified from playing the ingénue is a matter of much speculation in thespian circles. See **juvenile lead**.

inheritance factor Programme planning term to describe a number of viewers who carry on watching a particular channel after one highly popular programme has come to an end.

inject An item from a distant studio or location broadcast live as part of a news programme.

inker Artist in an animation studio who copies artwork on to cels.

inky dink/inky A small incandescent spotlight used for close-up illumination of small objects.

inlay Method of combining two pictures to form a composite using a third monochrome source as the switch or key.

inlay trolley BBC term for a portable unit containing the inlay monochrome camera and ancillary electronics to enable it to be used in any studio as a key source.

insert Piece of recorded film or video dropped into the main body of a TV studio programme.

insert editing/mode The method of videotape editing where a control track is first recorded on the tape so that pictures or sound may be dropped in and out at will without disturbing the pulses.

insertion test signals (ITS) Waveforms inserted into the field blanking lines of a television signal to test picture quality.

inserts (USA) See **cutaway.**

instant lettering (USA) Rub-on white or black lettering generally referred to in the UK by the trade name of Letraset.

intake desk Section of newsroom responsible for incoming copy from correspondents, etc.

intensity The brightness of a light source.

inter-cut To cut repeatedly between two or more images, e.g. interviewees during a recorded documentary programme.

interactive video Recorded video disc with which a viewer may pursue a dialogue with the aid of a computer. A sophisticated teaching machine, but having many possibilities for broadcast television with the spread of cable TV.

interchangeable lenses Lenses of fixed focal lengths which may be dismounted and interchanged. Opposite of **zoom lenses**.

intercom **1.** Cable or radio communications system between the various production and technical areas. **2.** (USA) Talkback.

interface Link between dissimilar electronic/mechanical pieces of equipment.

interference Unwanted electrical signals causing sound or picture distortion.

interior shot Shot taken on an indoors location or a studio set simulating an exterior.

interlace scanning The process of building up a frame of picture by two fields, the first scanned on alternate lines, the second filling in the gaps between those lines, a method of effectively doubling the flicker rate, rendering it virtually invisible.

intermittent action The stop-go mechanism of a camera or projector which pulls each frame of film into the gate for exposure or projection, but which moves so fast as to deceive the eye and give the impression of continuous running.

internal balance Editorial decision in a potentially controversial programme to ensure that both sides of an argument are equally represented without any appearance of bias by the programme makers themselves — sometimes an exercise in fence-sitting which pleases nobody.

International Broadcasting Convention (IBC) A bi-annual conference/exhibition used to launch new products in Europe. See **National Association of Broadcasting/International Video and Audio Convention**.

international sound track Music and effects

track where a film is intended for overseas sales. Commentary or dialogue is omitted to leave room for dubbing in a foreign language.

International Standardisation Organisation (ISO) Co-ordinating international body for technical standards, e.g. film speeds, etc.

International Video & Audio Convention (IVAC) A bi-annual conference/exhibition used to launch new products in Europe. See **National Association of Broadcasters/International Broadcasting Convention**.

internegative Negative copy taken from a master and then used to make a series of prints.

interpositive Colour master print taken from the original negative and then used for further negatives.

interrupted feedback (USA) Switched talkback facility in a studio, sometimes called **program interrupt**.

interrupted pan A shot where the camera pans with a moving subject but suddenly reverses direction to reveal some new information, e.g. a slow pan left to right following the cavalry followed by a sudden pan back to the left to reveal the Indians hiding in the grass.

intervalometer The adjustable timing device which is used to control the shutter in time lapse photography.

Intervision Eastern Block European counterpart to Eurovision, a programme-sharing international organisation.

intro/outro Scripted or recorded spoken introduction to a previously recorded story or programme.

invercone Translucent cone fitted over an exposure meter for measuring incident light.

inverse square law Mathematical principle

which explains how light falls off progressively the further the subject from the light source, e.g. at twice the original distance from the lamp a subject only receives one quarter of the original illumination.

invisible cutting (USA) See **A and B roll printing/working**.

invited guest A celebrity who appears on a hosted television show to be publicly flattered. Uninvited guests are not referred to in programme publicity.

iris The variable aperture of a lens which can alter the amount of light falling on the film or camera receptor by opening and closing.

iris wipe A wipe in which one picture wipes to another by expanding or diminishing round a porthole, like the opening and closing of a camera lens aperture.

island site BBC regional television station responsible for feeding local news to London and producing local programmes.

iso (USA) Pronounced EYESOH. Recording with two or more electronic cameras where each shoots independently on its own dedicated video recorder. Not to be confused with **ISO**.

isolating transformer A transformer with separate primary and secondary windings which isolate a mains electricity supply for safety purposes.

J PM See **jolts per minute**.

jack/jackplug Plug consisting of insulated concentric rings of conductors used particularly for sound interconnections.

jack up To improvise something in a hurry.

jack up level To increase the volume of a signal.

jackfield A bank of sockets for jacks which permits swift access to all the relevant inputs and outputs of sound equipment and lines using cables with jackplugs at both ends.

jackpoint A place in a jackfield where a jackplug may be inserted.

jam To attempt to render inaudible a transmitted signal by transmitting an interfering signal on the same frequency.

jelly Coloured filter on a lamp. See **Cinemoid**.

Jensen A piece of equipment used to synchronise a film camera with an electronic monitor.

jib 1. (noun) The swinging arm mounted on a camera crane or dolly. See **crane**. 2. (verb) To elevate or swing a camera mounted on a jib arm.

jingle Short distinctive piece of music used to identify a programme, TV commercial, etc.

jitters 1. Irregular fluctuations in pulse timings. 2. Jumping of film in a projector gate. 3. Fluttering on a video picture. 4. The jerkiness observable in poorly done, cheap animations.

jobsworth Petty official, frequently wearing a peaked cap, who says '*you can't do that, it's more than my job's worth*'. See **programme prevention officer**.

jock A disc jockey.

jog To make a small adjustment to the rest position of a sound or videotape to ascertain precise cueing. Equivalent of **inching** in film.

join A splice between two film shots.

joiner Mechanical device for editing two pieces of film together.

jolly A trip by a member of a production to an exotic location for barely justifiable reasons.

jolts per minute (JPM) (USA) Way of judging programme by the number of dramatic climaxes deliberately written into a script to hold the audience's attention until the next commercial.

journalist 1. Originally a writer, reporter or correspondent for a newspaper or magazine, but in news and current affairs television frequently a presenter and director. 2. A member of the National Union of Journalists. See **hack**.

joystick Remote control for a camera or a positioner built into a mixing desk.

juice Electric current.

jumbo cards Cards with script words or cues written in large letters and held next to the camera for presenters or actors who forget their lines. See **idiot card, crib card, cue card**.

jump cut A cut which breaks continuity by abruptly leaping in place or time revealing the same people or objects in new places or attitudes.

jump plates Hinged flaps, detonated by compressed nitrogen, used to propel stuntmen into the air in simulated explosions.

jump the cue An actor or operator anticipating a cue and starting action or equipment too early.

junction Connection between two transmitted programmes normally filled by a presentation announcement. See also **common junctions**.

junction box A box in which cables are terminated and/or joined. Sometimes inaccurately used to refer to a fuse board.

juvenile/juve lead Young or youngish leading part in a drama with equally important roles for older performers. See **ingénue**.

K *See* **kilo.**
kc/s See **kilocycles per second.**
kHz See **kilohertz.**
kW See **kilowatts.**

keep running! **1.** Director's instruction to a cameraman not to cut but to continue the action or instantly repeat a take without a board. See **flagging. 2.** Director's instruction to videotape or telecine to continue despite a gap in programme material.

Keesings Contemporary Archive A British compendium of world events much used by news researchers.

Keller Dubbing theatre system where the picture appears on electronic monitors in place of a film projection screen.

Kelvin Measure of temperature based on absolute zero (-273 centigrade), i.e. temperature in degrees Kelvin is degrees Centigrade plus 273.

kestrel Small camera crane with a seat for the operator alongside the camera at the end of the jib arm.

key and lamp Popular form of telephone exchange usually without the confusion of ringing bells. Favoured by newsrooms.

key grip Chief grip on a feature film or large television programme.

key light Main modelling light on a subject, used usually with a backlight and a filler light.

key numbers Alternative term for **film edge numbers.**

key shot (USA) See **master shot** .

key station (USA) Station which originates a programme for subsequent distribution by a network.

keyholing Lens fault giving soft focus round the edge of a television picture.

keying 1. Adding a modelling light to a subject. **2.** Activating an electronic switching signal to switch into one picture a picture from another source the exact sync and shape of the switching signal.

keying colour Colour chosen to activate chromakey backgrounds, most commonly blue.

keying signal The switching signal used to activate chromakey or CSO.

keystoning Distortion of a projected image causing the vertical sides to converge towards the top or bottom caused by the incompetent alignment of a projector.

kicker Light placed low and to the rear of the artist on the opposite side to the key light to enhance modelling effects in portraiture.

kill To remove anything unwanted on the set or to turn off a light or other equipment.

kilo Term denoting thousands, e.g. a budget of ten thousand pounds = 10k.

kilocycles per second (kc/s) Obsolete term for kilohertz (thousands of Hertz)

kilohertz (kHz) A thousand Hertz.

kilowatts (kW) Thousands of watts, a measurement of electrical power consumption. In lighting, generally an indication of the size and power of a lamp. Often referred to as ks, e.g. = 2k, 5k, etc.

kine Original spelling of cine, relating to film. Survives in some areas, e.g. telecine is abbreviated as TK in the BBC (TC everywhere else) to avoid confusion with Television Centre (TC).

kinescope (USA) See **telerecording**.

kinestasis The use of still pictures in animation. See **benchwork, rostrum**.

Kirby wire Patent system of wires and harness

used mainly on the stage to achieve Peter Pan-type flying effects.

Kliegs (USA) A range of stage and television lights.

knee Means of extending the contrast handling range of an electronic camera.

knee shot A loose mid shot which cuts off the subject at knee level, much used on American television. Described as **American shot** in some countries.

knockdown Prefabricated, portable dressing room carried around locations.

knocking copy A commercial which either deliberately parodies the commercials of a rival product or else makes invidious comparisons with the competition.

Kodalith Type of photograph paper used in graphics work.

L **/A** Script abbreviation for **low angle**.
laser See **light amplification by stimulated emission of radiation**.
LE See **Light Entertainment**.
LED See **light-emitting diode**.
LMCR See **lightweight mobile control room**.
LP See **long play**.
LS Abbreviation for **long shot** or **loudspeaker**.
LWT See **London Weekend Television**.
laboratory Workshop where film is processed and graded, and optical effects are produced.
lab report Report returned after processing by a laboratory to the film editor commenting on technical quality.
lacing up The act of running the film from the feed spool to the take-up spool in a projector, camera or editing machine.
lag Smearing of a picture on a screen caused by the physical properties of the camera tube.
lambert Measurement of luminosity of a light source.
lamp A source of artificial light. Sometimes used to describe a complete housing; at other times for just the bulb or source itself.
landline Interconnection between two locations by cable.
Landsat The name of an orbiting satellite.
landscape General term for real or contrived scenery used as a background.
landscape format Rectangular-format photograph composed horizontally. Opposite of portrait format in which the composition is made vertical by rotating the camera through 90º.
lantern An alternative term for a luminaire or lamp.
lanyard mike Personal microphone worn around the neck on a lanyard; largely superseded

by the miniature clip-on personal mike. See **lavalier**.

lap dissolve A visual effect in which one image replaces another by gradually increasing in brightness as the other darkens to invisibility.

lapel mike An unobtrusive personal microphone which can be clipped on to a performer's clothing.

Laservision Patent system employing lasers to read discs.

latent image Image on the emulsion of an exposed piece of film not yet made visible by chemical development.

latitude 1. The range of apertures and shutter speeds in which a satisfactory exposure is possible. **2.** The capacity of a film or videotape to represent the subtleties of colour and light gradation.

launch The staged event at which a new product or programme series is introduced to the press and public.

lavalier mike A lanyard microphone, named after Madame de laVallière, a French royal mistress with a penchant for necklaces.

lavender Finegrain positive film stock used for making duplicate negatives.

lay on To arrange news coverage of an event.

laying sound The process of laying a series of sound tracks on a pic sync alongside the edited pictures prior to the final mix at a dub. See **track-laying**.

lazy-arm A fixed boom with a counterweight for suspending a microphone in a studio.

lazy-tongs See **pantograph**.

lead 1. A cable connecting two pieces of mobile equipment. **2.** Information about an event or future happening which can be followed up.

lead singer Main singer in a pop music group. In television may be the only performer to sing live on air while the rest of the group mimes to a backing track.

lead story Story at the front of a programme, judged by the editor to be the most important in a topical magazine programme.

leader Length of film at the beginning and end of a reel enabling it to be laced and synchronised on an editing bench or projector. Front leaders have printed countdowns in feet or seconds.

leg Unframed length of curtain used on the end of a flat to stop cameras shooting off or the audience seeing into the wings.

legs 1. Cameraman's term for a tripod.
2. News term for a story that will continue for a long time, as in '*this story has legs*'.

lens Optical glass through which the light passes to define images on film or electronic tube.

lens angle The horizontal angle of acceptance of a lens.

lens aperture See **aperture**.

lens cap A metal or plastic disc used to cover the front of a lens.

lens change The ability to replace one lens with another. See **prime lenses**.

lens hood Hood mounted in front of a lens to prevent unwanted reflections from oblique sources of light.

lens mount Gizmo for attaching a lens to a camera body, e.g. C-mount, bayonet mount, etc.

lens speed Description of the *f* number of a lens at its widest aperture; therefore a way of describing its light-gathering capacity compared to other lenses of similar characteristics, e.g. a fast lens is essential in low-light conditions.

lens turret System where up to 4 or 5 prime lenses can be mounted on a plate which can be rotated on the front of a camera. Largely superseded by the introduction of zoom lenses.

lenticular screen Highly reflective screen covered with small spherical beads directing the light in a particular direction. See **axial front projection**.

Letraset Patent brand of adhesive lettering once much used on caption cards for name captions in television, increasingly superseded by electronically-generated graphics.

letterboxing Means of masking top and bottom of wide screen cinema films for normal television format screen transmission.

level 1. The strength of an audio or video signal. **2.** Audio recordists will ask for lines of dialogue for 'level' in order to adjust their equipment prior to recording.

level test Routine preceding a recording in which sound levels are tested and adjusted.

libel Defamation in a permanent form. Before the advent of television and radio, this meant in writing but now covers all the media.

library footage/shots Footage or shots acquired from a collection of archive film or videotape material rather than specially-shot material.

library music Specially-recorded background mood music, without copyright clearance problems, available on disc.

libretto The story and words of an opera or other musical production.

licence fee An annual levy on the viewing and listening public which entitles them to receive broadcast programmes. The means whereby the BBC is funded.

lift Control of an electronic camera for setting the black level in a scene .

lift off layback (USA) The laying of a sound track over a mute cutaway shot in a scene with continuous sound.

light amplification by stimulated emission of radiation (laser) A means of generating a pure and concentrated beam of light. Used for scanning video discs, holograms, etc.

light beam 1. A beam of light. **2.** A section-alised metal joist which can be assembled on location to support a heavy overhead lighting rig.

light box A box with a translucent screen lit from below, used to inspect film transparencies.

light emitting diode (LED) Semi-conductor light source.

light end Part of a film processing machine which may be safely exposed to white light as opposed to the dark end where the film is loaded and the early stages of processing occur.

Light Entertainment (LE) Name for production departments producing undemanding and amusing programmes; quizzes, comedy or popular music.

light level The overall intensity of illumination of a complete scene or location.

light pen An electronic sensor resembling a pen that can be used to draw directly on to a screen. Used extensively in video graphics.

light trap 1. Device for excluding light whilst loading a camera or processing machine. **2.** A revolving or double door system acting as a light lock between illuminated and dark rooms in a processing laboratory .

light valve An electronic device used to control modulations whilst recording or printing optical sound.

lighting The artificial illumination of a scene to achieve a naturalistic or creative effect.

lighting cameraman Principal cinematographer of the unit responsible for film lighting. Often has a camera operator working under instruction.

lighting console Board which controls the brightness of studio lights and usually permits pre-setting of a lighting combination. Portable versions are sometimes used on location.

lighting director Person responsible for the creative aspects of lighting.

lighting plan/plot A studio plan showing the lighting grid of a studio in relation to the floor on which the lighting director can plot the position of the lamps.

lighting pole stick Long pole which can pan, tilt and focus lamps that are out of arms reach.

lighting ratio The mathematical equation of the intensity of the key light divided by that of the filler light on a scene.

lighting supervisor An alternative term for **lighting director**.

lightmeter Apparatus for measuring incidental and reflected light. An exposure meter.

lightning effects Sudden lighting changes in the studio or flash frames in film used to simulate lightning.

lightning stick Arc lamp used to simulate lightning or explosions.

lightweight mobile control room (LMCR) A control room facility built into a specially-adapted vehicle that supports vision facilities, several lightweight cameras, production and sound control and sometimes VTRs.

lily Type of grey scale chart used by engineers for testing cameras.

limbo black/white (USA) Background — an unadorned set with black floor or white floor and black drapes or white cyclorama, lit to apparently suspend the action in space. See **infinity cyclorama**.

limbo shot Cinematic technique of lighting a character in the foreground against a totally black background.

limiter Device for automatically preventing sound or picture signals exceeding pre-set limits.

limpet mount Camera mounting attached to a rubber suction pad used on vehicles for travelling shots.

line Telecommunications circuit between a point of transmission and a point of reception.

line microphone (USA) Rifle mike.

line of action/axis Imaginary line which divides a scene into two 180-degree segments. So long as the camera or cameras remain within one segment, a sense of geography between characters stays constant, regardless of the shots. Failure to observe this leads to a disorienting effect called **crossing the line.**

line pairing Television display fault in which the lines making up the picture no longer seem equally spaced, so they become much more noticeable.

line rehearsal (USA) See **read-through**.

line resolution The maximum resolution of a picture, usually expressed in lines/mm.

line scan The electronic signal that creates the horizontal component of pictures.

line standard The number of lines used to make up a television image. In USA and Japan 525 lines, elsewhere mainly 625 lines. The more lines the greater the definition of the picture. See **high definition television.**

line-up time 1. In electronics studios the time taken immediately before recording or transmission for engineers to balance the output of their cameras. Also used to describe more fundamental adjustments to cameras at other times to achieve optimum performance. **2.** In film, the business of mechanically arranging camera positions, rails, focus, pulls, etc, as a technical rehearsal prior to a take.

linear When signal output from a device is exactly proportionate to the signal input.

liner Cosmetic make-up pencil used to outline eyes, lips, wrinkles, etc.

lines Dialogue in a script delivered by an actor or presenter.

link A written bridge between two separate items in a magazine or news programme.

link man A journalist or other presenter who appears in vision to link verbally the different items in a magazine programme.

links van See **comms van**.

lip flap (USA) See **goldfishing**.

lip mike Hand microphone, held close to the mouth, used by sports reporters in noisy environments.

lip sync Perfect synchronisation of sound and pictures especially in dialogue.

liquid crystal display Low-energy means of displaying numbers and letters familiar to owners of digital watches.

liquid gate Film printing system where liquid is interspersed between negative and print stock to mask any negative damage.

liquid head See **fluid head**.

Listener, The Weekly publication containing edited transcripts of radio and television programmes as well as comment and criticism.

lit area The area of action that the lighting director has agreed at planning meetings and rehearsals will be lit .

live 1. Switched on electric connection or faded up studio microphone. 2. A programme transmitted as it is happening without any delay or editing.

live acoustic Sound characteristic of a location with a preponderance of sound-reflective surfaces.

live action Real action as distinct from pre-recorded or simulated action.

live audience Invited or paying audience recorded at an event or studio.

live on tape (USA) A recording of a performance subsequently transmitted as though live and unedited.

live walls False walls built on location which can be easily struck and replaced.

live-as-recorded Description of a recorded programme implying that it is presented in its entirety exactly as it occurred, though often used to describe an audience show which has been only lightly edited.

lively An acoustic which contains plenty of reverberation from walls and fittings.

load 1. The impedance across a power supply. 2. To call up a computer programme from disc or tape.

loading Placing of film or tape in the machine prior to a take.

Locam Special camera used for very high-speed photography, that is for slow motion effects.

location Any venue for a shoot outside the studio, sound stage or the specially-constructed backgrounds of the film lot.

location catering Refreshment provided on an outside location for crews and performers normally by specialist professional caterers. See **chuck wagon**.

location finders Professional agencies which supply lists and scales of fees for film and television locations.

location index A list of researched locations with details and fees, kept by a broadcasting organisation or a location finding agency.

lock off To establish the camera on the tripod in the required position and then mechanically lock it in place to avoid the possibility of any movement during a take.

lock on The synchronisation of two autonomous sets of pulse-driven equipment.

lock-up time Time taken for a videotape machine to run mechanically up to operational speed.

log Daily record of studio activities, technical problems, etc, kept by the principal engineer in a TV studio.

log sheet Detailed technical record of a shoot prepared by the cameraman for the information of the laboratories and/or the editor.

logging shots Listing shots from rushes or VT and noting key numbers, rubber numbers or timecode and checking against any shot lists made during filming.

logo Easily identifiable symbol peculiar to a programme and usually incorporated into a set or titles.

London Weekend Television (LWT) London commercial TV company with a franchise for broadcasting at weekends only in London area.

long focus lens General term for any lens with a narrow angle of view.

long play (LP) A vinyl 12-inch diameter record that plays at 33 1/3 revolutions per minute.

long shot (LS) Shot taken with the camera placed well back from the object or scene. Composition of a shot showing the whole human figure.

looking room The area in front of the composition of a profile or half-profile shot unfilled by the face. See **nose room**.

loop 1. A length of film or magnetic tape joined at the ends which may therefore be played repetitively. Sound loops are often used in dubbing theatres to maintain a continuous background sound in long sequences. **2.** The length of film in a projector or camera between two points of the driving mechanism.

looping Term for post-sync dubbing of dialogue so-called because films used to be broken into 30-second loops and played repeatedly until an actor could perfectly match his voice to the original lip movements. Modern automatic dialogue replacement techniques avoid the necessity of breaking down film, but the term looping is still current.

loose shot A shot in which the subject is not framed tightly and therefore leaves a large empty space around the subject.

loosen shot To leave a greater margin between the subject and edge of frame.

Lord Privy Seal Describes a syndrome of news programmes where there is a compulsion to illustrate every reference with a picture. Derives from the satirical show *That Was The Week That Was* when the title Lord Privy Seal was illustrated by successive images of (1) a belted Earl; (2) a lavatory seat; (3) a sea lion.

lose effects/super! Studio director's instruction

to get rid of sound effects or superimposed electronic captions.

lose it! Studio instruction to fade out of, pan away from or otherwise get rid of an image, piece of music, property, etc.

lot A permanent or semi-permanent film set built in the open, or the area outside a studio where such sets are put up.

loudhailer Electronically amplified megaphone used in directing action in crowd scenes and difficult locations. A **bull horn** (USA).

LORD PRIVY SEAL

loudspeaker A transducer for converting an audio signal into sound waves.

low band A format of U-matic video recorder on PAL/SECAM 625-line systems, generally used for semi-professional purposes.

low contrast filters Lens filter used to desaturate colours, soften contrasts and achieve pastel tones.

low key lighting Lighting with predominantly low luminance and deep shadows, but often with occasional highlights, e.g. scenes of night-time interiors.

low loader Flat-wheeled trailer on which a camera crew can work to shoot performances in a vehicle being towed behind or in the vehicle doing the towing.

low-angle (L/A) Shot taken from a low position, below the artist's eyeline. Often used to relate the eyeline of a standing artist to that of a seated one.

low -angle dolly Sometimes referred to as VLAD, Vinten low-angle dolly. A mobile camera mounting for low-angle shots.

low-pass filter Sound equipment for removing unwanted high frequencies from a recording. Also used in video circuits for a variety of reasons, e.g. to reduce high-frequency interference (noise) or separate luminance and colour information in decoders.

low-speed filming Filming when the film goes through the gate at a speed slower than the standard 24/25 frames per second which, on projection, will give a speeded-up effect. Also called **undercranking**.

lower loop The loop of film formed after passing through the gate of a projector prior to passing the sound heads.

lower magazine (USA) A spool box or take-up magazine.

lower third The bottom part of a TV screen divided into nominal thirds as a means of describing good composition of the human face. The area in which name captions are normally superimposed.

lower-third captions Names and identification graphic captions superimposed over mid or mid close up shots of participants in a programme.

lumen A measure of luminous flux from a light source.

Lumière Brothers French proprietors of the first chain of commercial cinemas from the 1890's and pioneers of the cinema.

luminaires Studio or stage lights.

luminance 1. Measure of reflected or radiated light from a surface. **2.** The part of a wider signal that relates to brightness, as distinct from chrominance which relates to colour.

luminous flux The radiated energy from a light source, measured in lumens.

lux Metric measure of illumination used to replace foot candles, equivalent to the incidence of one lumen per square metre.

Lynx Portable monochrome television camera used mainly for closed circuit work.

M **& E** See **music and effects**.
MAC See **multiple analogue component**.
MATV See **master antenna TV**.

MC See **master of ceremonies**

MCB See **miniature circuit breaker**.

MCR See **master/mobile control room**.

MCPS See **Mechanical Copyright Protection Society**.

MCU See **medium close-up**.

MHz See **megahertz**.

MOMI See **Museum of the Moving Image**.

MPRC mole See **mole**.

MS Script abbreviation for **mid-shot, medium shot**.

MU See **Musicians Union**.

MVTR See **mobile videotape recorder(s)**.

Mac Marker A make of electronic clapperboard.

Macguffin Term coined by Alfred Hitchcock to describe the central device around which all the rest of the plot revolves, i.e. an incriminating document, a stolen object or a dead body as in his *The Trouble with Harry*.

machine gun (USA) An extremely long, highly directional rifle microphone.

macky (USA) See **maquillage**.

macro lens Lens capable of extreme close-up work.

macrophotography Extreme close-up photography using special wide lenses or attachments. Not to be confused with microphotography which involves the use of microscope attachments.

mag-opt print A film release print which carries both magnetic and optical film sound for use by either type of projector.

magazine 1. Lightproof box containing the film which clips on to a camera. 2. A compartmentalised slide carrier for a stills slide projector. 3. Programme containing a selection of different items that are usually held together by link men or presenters. An inexpensive form of television and the usual format for topical programmes.

magenta The blue/red mix of prime colours, complementary to green.

magic arm Multi-jointed arm to support a French flag in front of a lamp or camera.

magicam (USA) Sophisticated system for complex chromakey effects in which the camera for the background is slaved to the foreground shot.

magnetic board A magnetic board that will accept metal backed letters and figures for immediate captions. Superseded by electronic character generators.

magnetic centrifuge Gramophone pickup employing a moving magnet.

magnetic film Sprocketed film magnetic sound track used in sepmag systems.

magnetic recording Recording on tape covered with a magnetic oxide, either for video or sound.

magnetic sound track Film sound reproduced on metal oxide as opposed to an optical sound system.

magnetic stripe Film with a strip of magnetic sound track material physically alongside the picture. See **commag**.

magnetic tape Oxide-coated tape on which sound or video pictures are recorded.

main title The leading caption announcing the name of the programme or film. Often superimposed over action shots or stills.

make and break Temporary scenery made for use on a single scene and then destroyed.

make-up 1. Cosmetics used by performers. **2.** The assembly of a single roll of different film or videotape stories prior to the transmission of, for example, a magazine or news programme.

make-up man (USA) Term for a film or VT editor on a magazine style show, who syncs up and assembles the roll of recorded inserts for playback in sequence by VT or TK/TC.

male plug Plug with projecting connectors which fit into the sockets of a matching female plug.

Maltese cross Part of intermittent transport mechanism on a good quality camera or projector.

manual control Control of a lightweight video camera lens iris by the cameraman not using the automatic features of the camera.

maquillage French for make-up, sometimes in American English shortened to **macky**.

March of Time 1930's American cinema newsreel remembered for its use of dramatic reconstruction to recreate or amplify contemporary events where actual news footage was unavailable.

mark A prepared spot on the set for an actor to begin or end a movement.

mark it! 1. Instruction given by a cameraman to an assistant to operate the clapperboard in shot. **2.** A studio instruction to mark furniture and actors' positions on the floor.

marking up To outline the floor of a rehearsal room with adhesive tape to give an accurate indication of the dimensions of a set.

marking-up tape Coloured adhesive tape used for marking up rehearsal room floors.

married print A print with either optical or magnetic sound physically printed along the edge of the picture. Also called a **combined print**.

married track (USA) Final mix at a sound dub.

marrying Laboratory process of combining separate sound and picture tracks to make a comopt or commag print for distribution.

mask 1. For one actor to step between another and the camera or audience so obscuring him from view. **2.** To block out part of a set or a source of light with a flat or drape. See **shooting off**.

masking 1. The process of deliberately covering part of an exposure for special effects. **2.** Blacking out part of an image or setting the limits of the printing or projection of an image. **3.** Laboratory term for the technique of correcting colours in a film.

mass audience programme A programme aiming to satisfy the tastes of the whole viewing population. See **soap opera, family viewing, schlock**.

mass medium Any channel of communication to a significant percentage of the population, i.e. newspapers, television, radio.

Masseeley Type of hot-letter printing press used to generate TV name captions on caption cards, increasingly superseded by electronically-generated letter captions.

master 1. A film print positive from which high-quality duplicate negatives can be made. **2.** VT. See **master tape**.

master antenna television (MATV) (USA) System of distributing signals from a single aerial to a whole building or community using microwave transmitters and receivers.

master clock A precision clock to which all other clocks in a studio complex are slaved.

master control room (MCR) Usually a control room that controls the station output to a transmitter.

master neg The original negative of a film kept at the film laboratories. Dupe negs are used for optical printing purposes to avoid possible damage to the original.

master of ceremonies (MC) (USA) A programme presenter or compère.

master positive A graded print taken from an original negative and from which subsequent duplicates are made.

master shot Wide shot taken to encompass the complete continuous action in a dramatic scene with the intention of shooting additional close shots and cutaways later. Also called **cover shot**.

mastertape Videotape equivalent of a show print in film. The final edited version of a programme on VT.

master track The sound track of a completed programme from which copies are made.

match dissolve A mix in sound or vision either for effect in music or to disguise a jump cut.

matching shots Lining up two complementary close-ups so they have a similar size and composition, usually prior to intercutting two people in an interview.

matching transformer Apparatus for combining two devices with differing electrical impedances, e.g. a microphone and an amplifier.

matrix A routeing system that can connect sound and/or vision sources to one or more destinations.

matt finish Non-shiny finish to photographs, graphics, etc, which avoids lighting reflections and flares and which makes them easier to handle than glossy pictures in a studio.

matte An opaque mask limiting the area of exposed picture which allows two images to be subsequently combined, i.e. where foreground figures appear against a previously filmed background.

matte box Attachment to the camera in front of the lens into which filters may be mounted.

matte screen Projection screen with a reflective surface that gives much the same brightness viewed from any angle. See **beaded screen.**

matting flat Flattage built on a chromakey set behind which performers may walk to give the impression of a real three-dimensional location, e.g. a flat painted chromakey blue so positioned as to fit a pillar in a two-dimensional painting. See **chromakey.**

meat axe A pole on which a flag or metal plate may be manually held in front of a lamp to adjust the beam.

Mechanical Copyright Protection Society (MCRP) British body for monitoring copyright on the reproduction of recorded material on behalf of the record companies.

media hype The art of drumming up interest in a forthcoming production by press or publicity officers concocting sensational stories for the press, radio and television. See **plug.**

medium 1. The means of communication with an audience. **2.** A loosely-used journalistic term describing radio, television or the press — collectively known as the media. **3.** Someone with powers to communicate with those who have passed over, a talent similar to that of a TV producer.

medium angle shot (USA) A shot composed using the normal mid-range of a zoom lens.

medium close-up (MCU) The usual shot for interviewers, presenters or guests on a TV screen where the bottom of frame lies midway between the waist and shoulders.

medium frequency (MF) Radio frequency band between 500 and 1600 kHz.

medium long shot A camera shot of a person, the bottom of frame cutting below the knee. Also known as an **American shot**.

megahertz MHz One million cycles per second.

memory retention 1. The ability of a bright image to burn itself on to some types of camera tube if left static long enough. The picture remains partially visible when camera is panned. Vidicon tubes are very susceptible to this effect. **2.** The ability of some lighting consoles to retain their memorised combinations and dimmer settings even after switch-off.

mercury vapour lamp Type of lamp bulb containing vapourised mercury which gives a strong, whitish light.

mesh Part of a television camera pick-up tube.

message The overt political or commercial editorial content of a programme.

metal halide lamp Type of discharge lamp.

Method acting Russian and American school of naturalistic acting involving total psychological identification of the performer with his role, originated by the drama teacher Stanislavsky and popularised by the Actors Studio in New York.

metteur en scene French term for a director.

mic Script abbreviation for **microphone**.

mice Theatrical term for small microphones

concealed near the footlights particularly for speeches delivered downstage.

Mickey Mouse An odd expression meaning something amateur or less than well put together.

Mickey Mousing Film music term to describe the exact matching of action to dramatically descriptive music as in a cartoon film.

microwaves Extremely high-frequency radio waves.

microcinematography The use of a micro-scope attachment on a camera, as distinct from macrophotography which is photography at extremely close range using wide angle lenses.

microlink A radio link for small devices over a limited range, e.g. microphones.

microphone The apparatus used to convert sound waves to electronic signals.

microphone boom A telescopic microphone support frequently mounted on a wheeled base.

microphone gag See gag.

microphone shadow A shadow from the microphone thrown on to the walls of the set or other places where it will be in vision.

microphony Interference, usually on vision, caused by the sensitivity of some components to sound and vibration.

microscopic attachment A camera attachment used for microphotography.

microsecond One millionth of a second.

microwave dish A disc-shaped transmitting or receiving aerial for extremely high-frequency waves.

microwave link Point-to-point communication using extremely high-frequency radio signal.

mid-shot (MS) Shot of a performer composed from approximately the waist up.

mike/mic Abbreviation for **microphone**.

mike lead Cable connecting a microphone to a recorder or a fixed point in a studio.

mike tap Substitute for the clapperboard in a difficult filming situation, when the cameraman begins or ends a take by panning to the sound recordist who taps the top of his microphone in vision, so giving the editor a sync point.

milem A multi-image lens which can be rotated in shot for trick effects.

mime to playback Technique where musical groups perform to a pre-recorded sound track.

mimics A miniature replica of the studio lighting system in the lighting control room where small lights simulate the studio lighting combination. Also generally used for any remote indicator.

mini brute A large film soft light, normally made up of a number of individually switched bulbs.

mini pro A small, 500 watt luminaire.

mini series A drama series in which the episodes are transmitted consecutively on several nights in the same week.

miniature Scale model used to avoid the expense of building the real thing.

miniature circuit breaker A resettable fuse.

minicam Small mute film camera taking 50ft cassettes used for special action shots, e.g. bolted to the chassis of a vehicle, sky-diving equipment, or the like.

minijack Small jack plug particularly used with domestic equipment.

minimum focal distance The closest distance at which a lens can achieve focus.

Mirage A patent electronic effects device that permits three-dimensional manipulation of pictures.

mirror effect Trick effect giving multiple images by using mirror reflections. For its ultimate use see the climax of Orson Welles' *The Lady from Shanghai*.

mirror shot Shot using the reflection in a mirror. Customarily used to achieve overhead shots in studio demonstrations, e.g. cooking programmes.

mise-en-scène **1.** A screenplay. **2.** A setting or period for a drama.

mismatch Incorrectly adjusted equipment producing different results in identical circumstances, e.g. cameras not adjusted for identical exposure and colour reproduction or two microphones producing a different sound quality.

Mister Ten-Per-Cent A theatrical or literary agent.

Mitchell Type of large, 35mm film camera now little used for television purposes.

mix alternative term for a dissolve between two pictures.

mix down Mixing a large number of audio tracks to a smaller number, e.g. an 8-track master to a stereo pair of tracks.

mix for sound (USA) The combination of various sources or tracks in a studio or dub to produce a final sound track.

mix minus (USA) See **clean feed**.

mixed feed System for feeding the output of one studio camera into the viewfinder of another so enabling the cameramen easily to match shots.

mixed light Mixing daylight and artificial light.

mixer **1.** Part of a sound system which takes a number of inputs and allows an operator to combine and balance the volumes, as well as manipulate them to achieve a particular effect.

2. Electronic device for selecting vision sources and creating transitions, e.g. mix, wipe, between them. See **switcher**.

mixing console Studio sound desk at which audio inputs are controlled.

moat A sunken area in front of a studio cyclorama in which a lighting ground row may be concealed.

mobicrane Vehicle mounted camera crane for location shooting.

mobile base A mobile control room in an outside broadcast.

mobile control room (MCR) Transportable vision and sound production suite for TV and radio outside broadcasts.

mobile earth station Equipment to transmit signals from an outside broadcast to base, via satellite.

mobile unit Usually a portable talkback system carried by people on location, although sometimes used generally about any outside broadcast vehicle.

mobile videotape recorder(s) (MTVR) Videotape recorders housed in a vehicle at an outside broadcast.

mock-up 1. Non-functional copy used as part of a set: sometimes as small as a simulated piece of kitchen equipment in a cookery programme or as large as the interior of a passenger aeroplane in a feature film. **2.** Scale model of an intended set or construction created by a designer prior to approval for building to commence.

mode Redundant computer jargon for a function of a piece of equipment, e.g. a recorder is not just in playback, but is described as being in a 'playback mode'.

model shot Shot or sequence containing scale

models. Can be used in conjunction with specially constructed or projected backgrounds.

model stage Studio in which trick shots involving models are filmed.

modelling The artistic use of lights to bring out the structure of a subject or portrait and give an impression of depth.

modelling light The main light on a subject that brings out the form and texture of the subject.

modelscope Lens attachment derived from a medical endoscope used for extreme close-up work with models or natural history subjects.

mods/mod Modifications/to modify — often seen by programme makers as the ineradicable urge of engineers to take ready-manufactured equipment and work on it until it can perform functions which it was never intended to at the expense of those which it was. See **specifications, tweak**.

modulation The variations in a high-frequency carrier signal caused by the superimposition of a lower frequency audio or vision signal.

modulator /mod 1. The electronic circuit that combines an audio or vision signal with a carrier signal. **2.** A lighting effect that causes the brightness of lights to vary in sympathy with an audio signal, e.g. strobe lighting synchronised with the heavy beat of disco music.

modular Adjective used of an electronic device.

module A self-contained circuit mounted on an interchangeable chassis. An electronic device constructed with a number of modules for ease of servicing.

moiré A strobing effect on the television screen caused by interference between two regular patterns, e.g. a check suit which creates a frequency pattern close to sub-carrier frequency, which confuses the decoder in the receiver.

mole/MPRC mole A large motorised camera crane.

monaural Non-stereophonic sound recording.

monitor **1.** A television display (usually high quality) showing the output of cameras, etc. **2.** A high-quality loudspeaker for sound monitoring. **3.** To watch or listen to programme material closely and critically.

monitor cue Newsreader's cue taken direct from the pictures on the studio floor monitor showing the programme as it is transmitted.

monitor viewfinder Viewfinder external to the camera, but connected to it enabling a director or choreographer to watch the image as the camera is turning.

Monitoring Service BBC news gathering service operating from Caversham near Reading which listens to radio broadcasts from around the world and reports stories of importance to newsrooms in London.

monochrome Images in black and white.

monopod Single-legged camera support.

monopole Hanger from which a luminaire can be suspended.

montage French for film editing. In English, more precisely describes stylised techniques suggesting passages of time, tension, etc.

mood music Background music used to enhance the atmosphere of a scene. Almost universal in feature films and common in much television drama.

moonlighting Paid work done for one company by personnel under exclusive contract to another.

mos (USA) Script abbreviation for a **mute shot**.

Believed to be derived from Central European personnel working in Hollywood who said '*mit out sound*'.

mosaic Digital video effect resulting in an image being broken into patterns of coloured rectangles.

motion picture (USA) Ponderous term for a film.

motivated music Music linked precisely to a specific action on the screen. See **Mickey Mousing**.

motivated sound A sound effect cued by an action or words.

motor boating Low spluttering noise caused by instability in a sound amplifier.

motor drive Electrically-powered unit attached to a stills camera which automatically winds film on.

motorised sync Cutting room synchroniser powered by an electric motor.

mount 1. A carrier for a still frame or transparency. **2.** The device which connects a lens to the camera body.

mounting A camera support. See **tripod, pedestal, crane**.

mouse 1. Small hand-held device whose movements over a desktop convey instructions to a computer. An alternative to a computer keyboard system. **2.** A small microphone mounted on a stage at ground level. **3.** A type of safety catch required on all lifting hooks.

Moviecam Type of 35mm film camera.

Movietone Company that produced a cinema newsreel, now an archive film library.

Movietone frame Early term for Academy aperture, 35mm, standard image size.

moving coil mike Microphone working on the

principle of a coil suspended in a magnetic field. Used particularly for situations where robustness or immunity from overload distortion is important, e.g. on a drum kit.

Moviola A manufacturer of film editing equipment.

Moy Camera heads, numbering machines, etc, designed by Ernest Moy Limited of London.

Moy camera mount A geared camera head/mount requiring skilled operation and providing exceptionally smooth camera movements.

Moy numbering Synonym for film **rubber numbering**.

muddy Indistinct, muffled or distorted sound.

mugging Overacting for comic effect, deliberate over-playing to an audience or TV camera.

multi-burst A television test pattern consisting of a series of wedges containing frequency patterns across the broadcast spectrum for checking frequency response.

multi-camera technique Electronic studio or OB technique of using two or more cameras simultaneously and vision mixing between them during the action, as opposed to single camera film or video in which the images are shot separately and out of sequence, then reassembled by an editor.

multi-layer colour film The normal colour film stock in which the emulsion consists of a number of layers, each sensitive to different parts of the colour spectrum.

multi-media Reaching the audience through more than one channel of communication. In the educational field, use of video recordings, broadcasts and associated literature; in business exhibitions, the combination of tape, slide, film and projected video in a presentation.

multi-track recorder A recorder involving a number of sound heads, usually 6, 8, 16 or 24, capable of simultaneously recording a different signal on each head. Particularly used in music recording.

multi-tracking Where two and more sound tracks are recorded simultaneously, but separately, and then balanced in a final mix. The basis of most music recording.

multibeam Compact quartz iodide lamp.

multicore Cable with a number of separately insulated conductors within a single sheath.

multilateral Shared use of a communications satellite by more than two organisations.

multiple analogue component (MAC) System for transmitting high-quality, high-definition pictures.

multiple exposure Exposure of a film emulsion more than once to create the superimposition of one image over another.

multiplex The sharing of equipment electronically or mechanically, e.g. through mirrors or prisms.

multiplexer Multi-input, single or double output vision switching device.

multiscreen projection Achievement of wide screen effects by projecting connected images on to more than one screen at a time via synchronised projectors.

multisplit (USA) Electronic means of feeding a number of different picture inputs into a single screen split into sections.

multivision Audio-visual presentation using an assembly of adjoining screens or bank of monitors, either to make up a composite or present several images simultaneously. See **video wall**.

Mummerset Indistinct and exaggerated rural southern English accent adopted by actors called upon to perform rustic roles.

Munsell Colour system of giving a precise definition of colours by hue and saturation.

Muppet Large (up to life size) hand puppet made famous by the *Muppet Show* TV series. Now a term applied to any large glove puppet .

mural (USA) Photographic blow-up used as a background to a set.

Murphy's Law If anything can go wrong, it will. See also **Second Law of Television, bug, gremlin.**

Museum of the Moving Image Permanent exhibition for film and television history on London's South Bank.

mush Low level background sound.

Music Box Cable channel specialising in pop videos and musical films.

music chart Frame-by-frame breakdown of a music track necessary for animation artists to synchronise movement to music.

music circuit The main sound output from an outside broadcast or studio.

music & effects (M & E) Composite sound track made for film dubbing session involving music, sound effects and sometimes location dialogue, but excluding commentary. Vital for the preparation of subsequent foreign language versions.

music track Film sound track containing background music and sometimes vocals.

musical A dramatized story or operetta where the musical interludes are an integral part of the story line.

musical bridge A musical link between two dramatic sequences.

Musicians Union (MU) The British Union for musicians which negotiates minimum payments and conditions of work.

mute 1. Without sound. **2.** To cut or lower a recorded sound level.

mute board Clapperboard held with the clapstick outstretched indicating to the editor that there is no synchronous sound with the picture.

mute shot Shot taken without synchronous sound.

Muzak 1. Patent name used generally for any system of piped music used to anaesthetise shoppers in supermarkets. **2.** General term for any background music with little intrinsic merit.

NAB (USA) See **National Association of Broadcasters**.

NARAL See **Net Advertising Revenue After Levy**.

NATKE See **National Association of Theatrical and Kine Employees**.

ND filter See **neutral density filter**.

NFT See **National Film Theatre**.

N/G Script abbreviation for **no good**, used in multifarious contexts.

NTA See **news transmission assistant**.

NTSC See **National Television System Committee**.

NUJ See **National Union of Journalists**.

NAB adaptor Permits the use of NAB spools on the standard tape reel spindle.

NAB spool Standard dimension magnetic sound tape spool defined by the American National Association of Broadcasters. 10 1/2-inch diameter spool for quarter-inch tape with large central hole.

Nagra Swiss make of portable sound tape recorder particularly used in synchronisation with film cameras.

nanosecond A thousand-millionth of a second.

name card/super Identification caption superimposed over the image of a contributor.

narrator Commentator in a documentary-style programme whose words are normally spoken out of vision. Sometimes used as a device in drama where the narrator is the out-of-vision storyteller.

narrow angle lens Long lens/telephoto lens used to isolate a small detail of a scene.

narrow gauge Film term to describe generally all film widths narrower than 35mm.

narrowcasting Television programmes

designed to be received by a limited audience via cable, closed circuit, distribution of recorded cassettes, videodiscs, etc, as distinct from broadcasting via transmitters or satellites.

National Association of Broadcasters (NAB) (USA) Regulatory body which defines technical broadcast standards. Holds annual convention/exhibition, usually used to launch new equipment in USA.

National Association of Theatrical and Kine Employees (NATKE) Union primarily of cinema technicians, but to which many scenic and film operatives in television also belong. Now part of the Broadcast & Entertainment Trade Alliance (BETA).

National Film Archives Collection of library film material administered by the British Film Institute.

National Film Theatre (NFT) British public body, administered by the British Film Institute, which organises regular programmes of feature films, etc.

National Regions BBC stations in Wales, Scotland and Northern Ireland, which have a limited autonomy from London.

National Sound Archive Library of recorded sound. Official title is the British Library National Sound Archive.

National Television System Committee (NTSC) (USA) Standard for 525 lines American and Japanese colour television systems: dubbed by irreverent engineers as *'Never Twice the Same Colour'*.

National Union of Journalists (NUJ) Union of print journalists, to which many radio and TV newsroom journalists and others belong.

natlock A system of locking remote and local

pulse generators so that both sources are synchronous at the mixing point.

natural breaks (USA) Dramatic climaxes or scene changes deliberately written into a screenplay to allow for the insertion of commercials.

naturalism Predominant style of acting and direction in TV in which performances, sets and action are tailored to simulate everyday life.

neck microphone (USA) See **lanyard microphone**.

needletime Agreement between broadcasting organisations and the Musicians Union concerning the proportions of live and recorded music to be transmitted.

neg scratch A scratch on an original negative, usually caused by a foreign body in the gate of a camera, which makes a white scratch along the resulting print.

negative Processed film from which a positive is struck.

negative cutting/negative assembly Process of matching negative film with the cutting copy by using the edge numbers, before printing a show print.

negative picture The display of the negative before its conversion into a positive print or the deliberate electronic conversion of a video picture into a negative image for effect.

negative polarity One terminal of DC battery or source has a negative polarity, one has positive polarity.

negative timing (USA) Film grading in the laboratory.

negative track The negative of an optical sound track.

net A type of filter which softens the image whilst emphasizing highlights.

Net Advertising Revenue after Levy (NARAL) The declared profit after tax made by the British commercial companies. Network airtime is shared between them on the basis of individual NARAL ratings.

network Programmes broadcast nationally by a linked series of transmitters as distinct from those put out in a single region.

Network Committee Committee of executives of IBA companies responsible for deciding which programmes are selected for distribution. See **Big Five.**

Network Production Centres BBC English regions; Bristol, Birmingham and Manchester, which produce programmes for national network distribution rather than purely local products.

neutral density filter (ND filter) Filter used to cut down the brightness of a scene without affecting the tones or colours.

Neve British manufacturer of sound mixing desks.

New Wave Description of a school of predominantly French film directors regarded as experimental in the 1950's.

news agency Commercial agency, e.g. Reuters, which collects news information from around the world for sale to newspapers and broadcasting organisations.

news diary Diary of forthcoming events which is the basic source of forward planning in a newsroom.

news transmission assistant (NTA) Person responsible for scripts and working as the director's assistant in the gallery on news programmes.

newscast (USA) A news bulletin.

newsreader Presenter of a news programme.

newsreel film Journal of current affairs and topical events, originally shown as a regular item in cinema programmes and used for a long time later to describe television news programmes.

newsroom Office for editorial staff working on a news programme.

newswriter (USA) A sub-editor; a journalist based in the newsroom who writes scripts and assembles material.

Newton's Rings (USA) Interference of light in thin oil films, etc, which causes coloured rings/patterns.

Newvicon Specialist camera tube with high light sensitivity, mainly useful for security cameras or night recording.

ni-cad Nickel cadmium rechargeable batteries.

nickelodeon (USA) Early term for a cinema.

night filter A camera filter used to simulate night scenes in daylight. Gives a blue cast to pictures and considered less acceptable in modern cinematography than hitherto.

night for day Technique for lighting a scene filmed at night to look like daylight. Opposite of **day for night**.

Nike A large camera crane used either in studios or mounted on a vehicle on outside locations.

nine point five Obsolete gauge of film. The first film to be manufactured on safety film stock for the amateur market.

nitrate film stock Originally the base for film stock was cellulose nitrate, which becomes highly inflammable and degenerates into gun cotton with age. Replaced by less dangerous materials since the 1950's.

nodal head Special tripod head enabling the camera to pivot around the nodal lens point.

Used, for example, when wishing to pan in a glass shot.

nodal point The optical centre of a lens.

noddy Cutaway shot taken as a safety measure after a recorded interview where the interviewer is shown in close-up silently grinning or nodding. Generally an awful shot but useful for an editor to get over even worse jump cuts.

noise Random spurious signals generated by electronic equipment or caused by external interference that manifests itself as **grain** on video pictures (similar in appearance to film grain) or hiss on sound.

noise-cancelling mike Microphone designed to eliminate extraneous noise when used in close proximity to the mouth, e.g. by airline pilots.

noise gate Automatic switch which disconnects an audio input when it drops below a pre-set level.

noise level Level of unwanted, signals produced in all electronic devices, e.g. tape hiss.

noise reduction system Processing system to mask or reduce the effect of noise in a system, especially tape recording, e.g. Dolby.

non-additive mix A video mix where brightest content of one picture takes precedence over the other.

non-attributable Literary or recorded material for which the origin is traditional or unknown and for which there are no copyright implications.

non-composite picture A video picture with no sychronising pulses.

non-flam Not flammable. Specifically used to describe safety film stock.

non-linear amplifier An amplifier whose gain is related to the input signal amplitude.

non-practical Scenery or prop which appear real but are non-functional. See **mock-up**.

non-selective tracks Sound tracks on video-tapes dedicated to a particular function, e.g. time code on some videotape machines.

non-speaking extra A walk-on employed to perform without speaking.

non-sync cut A vision cut between two non-synchronous sources, often causing the pictures to roll.

normal angle The horizontal angle of view of a camera lens that most closely resembles that of the human eye, i.e. between 20 and 30 degrees.

normal focal length lens A lens producing an angle of view that has a similar perspective to the human eye (20-30 degrees).

north light A large soft light source in a scene.

nose room Area in the composition of a close shot between the tip of a nose in a profile or half profile shot and the vertical edge of the screen. Important in interviews and discussions where intercutting of images should convey the impression of people looking at each other.

notch Cut-out section on the edge of film which activates scene-to-scene changes of grading during the printing process.

Nouvelle Vague School of film direction. See **New Wave**.

number board (USA) Clapperboard, slate.

numbering machine Machine for printing reference numbers along the edges of synchronised film picture and magnetic sound prior to editing. See **rubber numbers**.

OB See **outside broadcast**

OB van Mobile control room for outside broadcasts

OOV See **out-of-vision.**

OR See **outside rehearsals.**

OTT See **over the top.**

OU See **Open University.**

oater Hollywood term for a Western movie or horse opera.

obit Obituary.

objective camera Style of drama direction usual on television in which the camera observes the action as an invisible spectator rather than simulating the viewpoints of the performers. See **subjective camera.**

octopus/Elemac octopus A widely used film camera dolly.

off Speech, sound or music delivered out of vision.

off air 1. Signals monitored by aerial from the transmitted signal instead of directly by cable. **2.** No longer transmitting.

off air monitor/receiver A receiver tuned in to the transmitted signal.

off air pictures Pictures received after broadcast transmission.

off camera Out of vision.

off mike Sound or dialogue delivered away from the microphone and generally unusable, but sometimes deliberately recorded to suggest perspective.

off scene/stage Sound of dramatic action which is taking place outside the picture frame. Not to be confused with OOV or out-of-vision, which is a news term for a commentary delivered without the reporter being seen.

off the air Generally refers to a series of

programmes in the periods when they have stopped transmitting but are anticipating a successive season.

off the wall An illicit sound recording, increasingly a term used to describe anything seemingly irreverent or experimental.

off-line editing **1.** System where a director, with or without assistance, views his rushes complete with time code and makes an assembly himself before going to final cut. **2.** Editing videotape using cheaper (non-broadcast) equipment which will allow several tape generations to be used. The quality is not affected as a master is then made up from the original rushes to match the final off-line edit. See **on-line editing**.

off-stage steps Out-of-vision steps giving access to a set for performers.

offers meeting Editorial meeting where producers compete for airtime and resources for the programmes proposed for the forthcoming year.

offset overlay A style of overlay where the complete background picture appears in a panel over the presenter's shoulder. More generally may refer to an overlay where the background is not centre of frame.

old Spanish customs General term for established irregular or unauthorised working habits which appear to be accepted as a matter of tradition.

omega wrap Tape path on the drum on a helical scan recorder shaped like the Greek letter omega, so allowing very nearly 360 degree contact between the tape and the record/play heads.

omni-directional mike A microphone that picks up sound through 360 degrees.

on a bell (USA) Film stage term to describe the period between the ringing of the studio warning bell and the director's call for action.

on air A programme is on air when it is being transmitted.

on-air light Red light at a radio or television studio indicating that a transmission or recording is taking place.

on camera A performance delivered in vision.

on lights! Gallery warning to studio cameraman that he is shooting into a luminaire with possibly disastrous consequences for the camera tube.

on stage On the set.

on the blink Any equipment having an intermittent fault.

on the fly Videotape editor's term for making a quick edit by hitting the edit button whilst the tape is playing.

on the nose/on the button The ending of a live transmission to the precise second of allocated time.

on the road Shooting on outside locations; being assigned work involving travelling from one location to another.

on-line editing Videotape editing using the original rushes to produce a transmission tape. Often used to refer to the process of conforming a transmission tape to a (low quality) off-line edited tape.

one light print (USA) See **single light print**.

opacity A measure of the degree of absorption of light, e.g. of a filter.

opaque Unable to let through light.

open circuit An incomplete electronic circuit due to a faulty component or broken wire.

Open College Educational programmes

intended for adult education and linked to publications, classes or correspondence courses.

open mike Microphone which is left faded up.

open reel A tape transport system containing separate feed and take-up spools instead of being enclosed in a cassette or cartridge. See **reel-to-reel**.

Open University (OU) Non-residential, degree-awarding university where the faculty keeps contact with the students by correspondence, television and radio.

open up To widen a lens aperture.

opening routine The first item in a programme intended as an audience puller, particularly in variety shows.

opening titles Sequence of film, graphics and music which identifies the beginning of a programme.

operator Any person who physically manipulates technical equipment.

opt-in/out! Orders given by a studio director on a live programme when a regional programme has to join or leave a continuing national transmission.

opt-out programme Programmes made by or for BBC Regions for local transmission which replace programmes on the national network.

optical barrier A synonym for the **line of action**. See **crossing the line**.

optical bench A metal track on which camera, lens and light box may be moved in relation to each other to film optical effects. See **rostrum camera, benchwork**.

optical printer Film laboratory equipment used to make reduction prints or special effects by projecting film and re-photographing it. See **contact printer**.

optical reduction Copying a film on to a smaller gauge using an optical printer.

optical sound track/system A photographic recording of the sound track which is printed alongside the picture. Used widely for feature film prints.

optical track The signals printed along the edge of a film print, which are read by shining a light through them. The normal sound system on cinema projectors.

opticals Effects on film like mixes, freeze frames and super-imposed titles carried out at the film laboratories using bi-optical printing methods after the main filming is completed.

optional cuts Items or script lines in a live transmission which may be dropped at short notice for timing purposes without obvious damage to the rest of the programme.

Oracle British Commercial TV Teletext system equivalent to the BBC Ceefax.

Orbita USSR television satellite system.

original 1. Shot film after processing.
2. Original video recordings from which an on-line edit will be made. See **master tape, off-line editing, on-line editing**.

original screenplay Filmic treatment of an idea, story or adaptation. May subsequently undergo rewriting several times.

Orthicon An early camera tube in general use until the late 1960's. Still used for specialist non-broadcast purposes.

orthochromatic film Black and white film sensitive to all colours except red. The main film stock of black and white movies.

Oscars Annual Hollywood prizes awarded by Academy of Motion Picture Arts and Sciences to the feature film industry.

oscilloscope An electronic instrument for graphically displaying signals and carrying out measurements of those signals.

out of focus 1. De-focused area of an image. **2.** Fuzzy or indistinct.

out of phase Error in timing or polarity of otherwise identical signals important to vision sources and stereo sound.

out of shot Out of vision/off stage.

out of sync Where picture and sound lose synchronism, e.g. when lip movements and words do not perfectly match.

out-takes The takes which are rejected when selecting shots in the cutting room — especially referring to those which contain gross mistakes and are the source of hilarity or embarrassment. See **Christmas tape**.

out-of-vision (OOV) Commentary or dialogue as sound only. (*pron.* OOOV).

outline A preliminary synopsis of a planned programme. See **treatment**.

output desk Section of newsroom or news agency concerned with completed and edited stories and their subsequent use or distribution.

outro Words spoken by a presenter at the end of an item indicating that that item is finished and a new subject will now be introduced.

outside broadcast (OB) Multiple video camera coverage of an event through a mobile control room. Known in America as a **Remote**.

outside rehearsals (OR) Drama production process conducted in rehearsal rooms prior to being brought to the studio or stage.

over-developed Film which has been left too long in the developing bath or at the wrong temperature resulting in a picture of exaggerated contrasts.

over-dub Build up sound on video tracks recording new information on an already recorded track.

over-exposed 1. To allow too much light to fall on a film frame or camera tube causing the bright parts of the image to merge together. **2.** Bleached-out image caused by the film being exposed for too long a period in the filming or printing process or on electronic cameras, too wide an aperture or excessive gain. **3.** Term dreaded by actors who have had a good run of successful parts on TV and are so deemed by producers to have been too much seen for their own good.

over-modulation An input signal greater than a piece of equipment can handle.

over the line See **above the line**, also **below the line, convertibility**.

over the shoulder shot A shot taken of one person from over the shoulder of another when the two are face to face, e.g. in an interview.

over the top (OTT) Term for anything viewed professionally as being excessively self-indulgent or extravagent.

overcrank To pass film through the gate at a speed faster than the standard 24/25 frames per second to give an artificial slow-motion effect on projection.

overhead lighting Lighting positioned directly above the action, usually from a studio grid.

overhead projector A projector used to project the image of a large size transparency from a desk on to a screen.

overlap The picture of an outgoing scene carried on over the sound of the incoming one, or vice versa.

overlay 1. See **colour separation overlay**.

2. A foreground cell in animation. **3.** Newsroom term for putting additional words or music over mute pictures.

overload **1.** Signal levels in excess of that which the equipment can handle, leading to distortion of vision or sound. **2.** Drawing too much power from a supply.

overpiece An architectural detail, such as an arch or roof detail, suspended from the grid of a stage.

overrun **1.** To use a light at a higher power than its intended wattage. **2.** When a production goes over its allotted time. In film this leads to heavy overtime costs, in studio it may result in production being terminated. See **pulling plugs**.

overscanning Display on television sets shown past the area of the screen to exclude the edges of picture. Used on domestic receivers.

overshoot To use considerably more film than the amount originally budgeted for or to exceed the agreed number of days shooting in order to complete a project.

overwritten A newsroom term for too many words and too few pictures.

P as B See **programme-as-broadcast**.
P as C See **programme-as-completed**.
PA 1. See **production assistant**. 2. See **personal/public appearance**. 3. See **public address**.

PABX See **private automatic branch exchange**.

PAL See **Phase Alternate Line**.

PBS See **Public Broadcasting Services**.

PBU See **photo blow-up**.

PCM See **pulse code modulation**.

PLUGE See **picture line-up generating equipment**.

PM See **production manager**.

PO jack A circular, two or three pole jack-plug with concentric contacts.

POV See **point-of-view**.

PPB See **party political broadcast**.

PPM See **peak programme meter**.

pps See **pictures per second**.

PR See **public relations**.

PSC See **portable single camera**.

PSM See **production services manager**.

PUMA See **periscope mirror**.

PZM See **pressure zone microphone**.

pacing The rhythmic arrangement of shots to maintain interest, provide appropriate climaxes, relax tension as appropriate, etc.

pack shot A shot in advertisements depicting the product itself in close up. Frequently the final freeze frame shot in a television commercial.

pack shot lens Close-up lens used for pack shots in commercials.

package To record a completely self-contained item or a magazine programme including introduction, illustrative material, opening and closing titles.

pad 1. A data keyboard or touch tablet used in computer graphics. **2.** An attenuator. **3.** To stretch an item of programme which is under-running to fill up the time available until the next cue or time slot junction.

paddock mount A small mobile camera crane used by O.B.'s on uneven ground.

page turn Video digital effect in which one image reveals another by appearing to curl and peel off the screen.

paint out To remove unwanted parts of a scene, e.g. TV aerials in a historical drama, using electronic graphics techniques.

painting-in Filling in prepared gaps in a film programme with exactly timed videotaped sequences and transferring a compilation to a master videotape.

paintbox Equipment for generating electronic graphics. The artist is in control of a palette of colours, which may be used to draw or paint freehand with an electronic pen.

paintpot Selection of synthetic colours which may be selected from the studio desk to change the colours of an image. Specifically used to colour captions and artwork which are originally prepared in black and white.

pan Abbreviation for **panorama**. **1.** Description of a camera move where the camera pivots from one side of a scene to another. **2.** In animation photography, describes a movement in any direction. **3.** To make a destructive, critical attack on a programme.

pan and tilt head The device between the top of a tripod and the base of the camera which enables smooth panning and tilting movements.

pan glass Selection of hand-held filters, generally neutral density filters, through which a cameraman can look at a scene to plan the lighting.

pan pot A control used in stereophonic sound dubbing for positioning the sound image to the left or right.

pan stick Foundation make-up in the form of stick, instead of a cake, of compressed powder.

panaglide (USA) Type of harness for steady hand-held camerawork.

Panavision Wide screen system of filming using 35mm film with an anamorphic lens or special 65mm film for Super-Panavision.

pancake 1. Foundation make-up in the form of a cake of compressed powder usually applied with a damp sponge. **2.** A reel of tape on a core. **3.** A low platform rostrum for artists.

panchromatic film Film sensitive to all the colours of the spectrum visible to the human eye.

panel 1. General term for a control board or console. **2.** Team of invited guests in a quiz or audience discussion show.

panic button A button on a studio gallery control desk which, in the case of technical breakdown, over-rides all the sophisticated functions whilst leaving the vision mixer the ability to do simple cuts between the cameras.

panning handle A tiller-bar at the back of a film or video camera head which the cameraman uses to control smooth panning or tilting actions.

Panstik (USA) Stick of greasepaint.

panther A sophisticated, small camera dolly with a computer-controlled central column which can be pre-programmed to elevate or depress during a shot.

pantograph Expanding tongs on which studio lights are raised and lowered.

paper up To choose selections of library film

from a long roll by marking the in and out points required with slips of paper wrapped round the film.

parabolic aerial An aerial using a parabolic dish to focus the signal in a given direction, e.g. a satellite dish.

parabolic microphone A highly sensitive, very directional microphone, where the sound is collected by a parabolic reflector and reflected into the microphone head. A typical use is on a cricket match to pick up close sound of bat on ball to match a close camera shot on a telephoto lens.

parabolic reflector A concave dish reflector for focusing sound, light or radio frequency signals.

parallax error Difference in the framing of an image seen through a non-reflex viewfinder and that seen by the lens — significant in close-up shots. See **reflex viewfinder**.

parallel action/development Basic editing technique of intercutting between two sets of action taking place simultaneously, but in different locations, often leading to a common dénouement.

partial shot Shot in which tension is built by showing part of an action but not its conclusion, e.g. a revolver being cocked and pointed but not the actual firing.

party political broadcast (PPB) A transmission devised and produced for a political party as part of their electioneering and normally transmitted on all channels. See **equal airtime**.

pass The number of times a piece of VT goes passed and remains in contact with the head in a recorder.

passing shot A shot in which the subject stays

still but the camera moves passed and through frame.

passive Electronic circuitry that requires no power to function.

passive satellite A non-activated satellite, usually one in orbit as a back-up to an operational satellite in case of failure of the primary satellite.

paste up Picture layout formed by a montage of pictures and text.

patch 1. To plug up studio lights, sound or vision sources or insert an electronic device, attenuator, etc, as required on the console or on a jackfield. **2.** Routeing of a signal from one station to another via one or more intermediate stations.

patch cord A short length of cable used to connect a source to a destination, whether lighting, sound or vision.

patch panel/board A panel of sockets to which sources and destinations are connected, so that interconnections can be carried out as required using a patch cord. Usually refers to lighting as distinct from a sound and vision jackfield.

patching The process of physically connecting sources to destinations using a patch cord.

Pathé News Cinema film newsreel available in the Pathé News Library.

Pathfinder Type of studio camera dolly.

patter 1. Well rehearsed verbal comedy routine. **2.** Inconsequential chat of a mindless nature. See **disc jockey.**

pattern generator TV line-up signal generator.

pause button Control on a videotape recorder which stops the tape transport without unthreading the tape. Can be used as a freeze frame facility on some machines.

Pay TV System of charging a viewer according to the hours of television actually watched by equipping the TV receiver with a meter.

pay-off Closing statement by a presenter in a magazine/news programme. See **thumbsucker**.

payola Unauthorised or illegal payments made for the insertion of promotional material, records or references into a programme item.

pea lights Strings of small lights like Christmas tree lights used in set dressing.

peak The maximum attainable value, e.g. peak white, in an electronic picture.

peak programme meter (PPM) Sensitive device for monitoring audio levels on audio mixers, tape recorders etc. See **vu meter**.

peak-to-peak Measurement of a signal wave from its positive peak to its negative one.

peaking into the red Sound volume reaching a level of distortion as shown on a dial.

peak viewing Time usually in the early evening when the potential viewing figure is judged to be at its maximum.

peak white **1.** An illuminated white surface whose reflectivity is the maximum that can be handled by a camera. **2.** The maximum electronic level of a video signal (0.7 volts) that corresponds to a peak white surface.

peak white limiter An electronic limit in a video signal that does not allow the signal to overload the transmission chain (0.7 volts). Any excessive signal, e.g. reflections from jewellery, will be limited to 0.7 volts.

pearl screen Highly reflective beaded projection screen. See **lenticular screen**.

ped Abbreviation for **studio camera pedestal**.

pedestal **1.** Electronic engineering term to define the electronic level at which scenic black is set (zero in Europe, 5% above zero picture level in USA). **2.** The standard one-man studio camera mounting which enables silent and fluid camera movements. The pedestal may be steered in any direction and the camera raised and lowered with ease on a gas-filled, counter-balanced column.

pedestal up/down To elevate or depress a studio video camera.

pee wee A type of small camera dolly.

peel Video picture defect, mainly produced on obsolete, image orthicon camera tubes.

peg The editorial reason or excuse for screening a story which otherwise lacks obvious topical content, e.g. *'this week is the anniversary of the Battle of Hastings and so our reporter has been down to investigate French restaurants on the south coast'.*

pegbar Device for keeping cels accurately

positioned for the graphic artist during the designing of animation graphics.

penalty payment Payment to a crew member for infringed working hours other than agreed overtime, e.g. financial compensation for missing a scheduled meal break.

Penthouse head Quadrophonic sound head used on 35mm stereo film projection systems.

Pepper's Ghost Old theatre trick. Action upstage is brightly lit and a translucent screen is positioned diagonally across a darkened down-stage. An image is projected obliquely on to this screen giving a ghostly effect.

perforation pitch The measurement between the edges of two successive perforations on a length of film.

perforations The sprocket holes along the edges of film stock.

performance fee The rate charged for appearing at a transmission or recording.

performance rights Legal rights vested in companies or individuals for recorded material, most commonly used to describe payments due for use of commercial gramophone records in programmes.

Performing Right Society The organisation charged with administering the legal and monet-ary aspects of performing rights, in particular the collection of copyright fees for composers, performers, authors and publishers.

period General description of dramas set in a specific historical time and place and demanding appropriate design costumes.

periodic noise Repetitive unwanted sound on an audio or video network.

periscope A lens attachment for a camera that enables very high or very low shots beyond the range of normal camera mountings or for looking over obstructions on location.

periscope mirror (PUMA) Periscope unit and mirror attachment. A BBC device that attaches to the lens of a studio or OB camera for very high or low shots. See **periscope**.

Perlux A patent, plastic, reflective surface projection screen.

persistence of vision Phenomenon of the eye and brain in which an image is retained in the memory briefly after it has physically vanished. The basis of all film and VT where different images pass before the eye so fast that the brain registers neither stopping nor starting nor the black bars between frames.

personal/public appearance (PA) Appearance by contracted personalities to open fetes, etc.

personal dish (USA) A domestic parabolic aerial for picking up programmes relayed via satellite instead of from land-based transmitters.

personal mike A small microphone normally attached to the wearer's clothing and often connected to a radio transmitter.

personal props Category of **action props**, specifically associated with an actor's wardrobe or appearance, e.g. monocle, cigarette holder, wristwatch, wedding ring, etc.

personality One down from a celebrity and much lower than a star but famous for the same reason though not as much so. Sometimes reduced to being a compère.

perspective 1. The ratio of direct to reflected sound from which the ear judges distance. Should always match the picture in drama, but this rule is sometimes broken in documentary programmes where clarity is more important. 2. Apparent depth within a set or in artwork, where the use of relative sizes and receding lines, apparently converging towards infinity, gives the illusion of three dimensions.

phantom power Technique of sending power to a microphone along the same wires that carry the audio output without creating any audible interference. Also used by TV camera cables.

phantoming Sending more than one signal down a single wire.

phase Measure of relative timing of two or more video or audio signals.

Phase Alternate Line (PAL) Development of the U.S. NTSC colour system to provide inherent correction for phase errors introduced in the transmission path which would otherwise cause incorrect displayed colours. See **Secam; PAL 1,** transmission standard for UK implementation of PAL 625 lines; **PAL M, PAL N,** other implementations using the basic PAL system with other line rates (PAL M) or sound carrier spacing.

phase lock Control of timing of video signals with respect to one another or a separate reference.

phasing 1. The adjustment of two coherent signals (sent as TV pictures or stereo channels) to be in exact time relationship. **2.** Interference of two mistimed audio signals, often used as an audio special effect created by delaying part of an audio signal then recombining it with the original, undelayed signal.

phone-in Type of programme particularly common on radio where the audience is invited to telephone and participate directly in the programme. The cheapest known form of broadcasting; popular with programme executives.

phono plug Small connector for coaxial wires used mainly for sound systems.

Phonographic Performance Ltd. Consortium of record manufacturers collecting copyright fees for broadcast sound recordings, e.g. **needletime**.

phosphor A chemical substance that emits light when bombarded with electrons.

phosphor delay Time taken for an image to die away after the electronic stimulation has been switched off.

photo blow up (PBU) Photographic enlargement big enough to be incorporated as part of a set or be used as scenic background.

photo-animation (USA) Technique of animating a set of still photographs with camera movements. See **benchwork**.

photo-caption Specially prepared photograph mounted on card and frequently combined with artwork or lettering.

photo-conductive The property of some materials to change their electrical resistance when exposed to light and therefore the essential material in modern camera tubes.

photo-electric cell/photocell A device for converting light energy into an electrical signal.

photo-electric emission The release of electrons on exposure to light.

photo-emissive The property of some materials to emit electrons when exposed to light.

photo-mounting press A machine for mounting photographs on card backings.

photodiode Light sensitive semiconductor used in light measuring devices.

photoflood Small, high-intensity light used on small locations mainly by stills photographers.

photogenic Someone who looks well on camera, often better than in the flesh.

photographic sound Optical film sound.

photometer (USA) A device for measuring light

intensity. A precision light meter.

photomural (USA) See **photo blow up.**

photon Unit of light energy.

pic sync/pixie Synchroniser used by film editors to match sound tracks and picture.

pick up a cue One artist reacts to a word or action cue from another.

pickup arm Balanced arm carrying a pickup head on a disc turntable system.

pickup head The device that tracks sound or video recordings on disc and converts them to an electrical signal. May be ceramic, magnetic or laser depending on the type of recording.

pickup tube Camera tube (vidicon, plumbicon, etc) that converts pictures into electrical signal.

pickups **1.** Shots taken later than the main shooting schedule to cover scenes unobtainable at the original time or to cover omissions later detected in the cutting room. **2.** Retakes, usually of bits of dialogue, after the main recording of a scene.

picture definition/resolution Sharpness of a picture or the amount of visible detail.

picture duplicate negative A negative derived from a print, usually because the original negative has been lost.

picture editor Film and videotape editor trained to operate with either medium.

picture element See **Pixel** .

picture grabbing Technique for taking a still frame from a videotape and employing it as a freeze frame or a component in a graphics sequence.

picture image The projected image on a screen.

picture lock (USA) Expression meaning the completion of picture and sound of a film or video: the point at which commentary can be written. See **phase lock**.

picture matching Ensuring colour and luminance grading of two or more video pictures.

picture negative Developed negative film from which prints can be obtained.

picture noise Random dots on the screen resembling film grain, particularly when video cameras are used in low light conditions or when edited tapes are several generations old.

picture release negative The negative used to make prints that are released for cinema distribution.

picture search Facility on videotape recorders and disc machines to locate a required frame either by controlled fast forward or reverse or by a programmed computer memory system.

picture signal The electrical signal representing the picture information that falls on the pick-up device (tube, photocell or CCD).

picture store A digital device which uses a digital store that can memorise one complete frame of picture and subsequently recall it during a programme.

picture sync ratio The ratio of the maximum picture voltage to the voltage of the synchronising pulses on a video signal, (normally 0.7 volt/ 0.3 volt).

picture tube Display device for TV set/ monitor.

picture weave (USA) See **ripple dissolve**.

pictures per second (pps) Measure of videotape speed in frames per second.

pie chart Graphic used to illustrate statistics. The whole is represented by a circle and the percentages expressed by segments of different colours similar to the slices of a pie.

piece to camera See **stand-upper**.

Piezo crystal A crystal that changes its electrical characteristics when stimulated by pressure. Used on early forms of record players and in certain types of microphones, as well as gas cigarette lighters, etc.

pigeon Courier charged with getting news film or tape from location to base.

pilot 1. An experimental programme or a trial first programme in a series recorded to test the viability of a project. 2. Colour test strip sent to a cameraman along with daily black and white rushes from the colour originals.

pilot pins See **pin registration**.

pilot tone A steady signal sent from the film camera to the sound recorder and recorded alongside the sound track. It is subsequently used at the sound transfer stage to keep film picture and sound in synchronism.

pilot track Rough spoken script or verbal cues used with the final stage of editing and track laying to assist with the fine cutting of pictures and laying of other tracks. Subsequently discarded and a final commentary put on at the sound dub. See **scratch commentary**.

pin cushion Geometric distortion of a television picture in which all four sides of the frame appear to bend towards the middle.

pin hinge Connector for flattage in the form of two halves of a hinge mechanism to be made fast by a removable metal pin.

pin registration The exact location of a film in a camera or projector by pins engaging in the sprocket holes.

Pinewood Large British film studio complex.

pipe To feed picture or sound from one place to another by means of a cable.

Pirate Unlicensed radio/television station transmitting illegally.

pirate video Unauthorised copy of a feature film or programme material.

pitch 1. Measurement of distance between two sprocket holes on a film. 2. Defined spot for setting up a news camera, e.g. to stake out a pitch, to get set up in anticipation of the action. 3. The frequency of a sound. 4. To compete for something, e.g. bigger budget, more air time, etc.

pitch changer Device for altering the pitch of audio signals to avoid the possibility of howl around.

pitch control Variable speed replay device in a sound recording studio used to facilitate the exact tuning of musical instruments.

Picture line-up generating equipment (PLUGE) A test signal that enables the brightness and contrast of monitors to be set accurately.

pix abbreviation for **pictures**.

pixel (picture element) The smallest divisible electronic elements making up a television picture.

pixillate To reduce the number of pixels in a picture, i.e. increase their size so that they become visible to the detriment of resolution. Used occasionally for effect.

pixillation An old film term referring to step frame animation of live action. Hence the term 'pixillated', meaning deranged. Nowadays refers to the television electronic effect of mosaic.

plan B The fallback plan for a production which hits problems. See **backup schedule, Murphy's law**.

planning meeting A meeting of production staff with a technical crew prior to taking a programme into the studio or on location.

plate 1. Rotating disc on a film editing desk on which the film tracks are placed. 2. A photographic print used as a master, often in composite shots. Term derived from the glass negative plates of early photography.

platen Sheet of glass used to hold down the layers of cels whilst building up an animation.

play to To act towards the audience or to a specific camera.

playback The reproduction of a recording, usually for review purposes or for performers or dancers to mime in synchronism.

plonking A style of newsreading in which words are delivered with a mechanical and monotonous rhythm unrelated to the meaning or syntax of the sentence.

plop Audible signal on the sound track of sepmag film timed to coincide normally with the four-second mark on a picture leader which tells the projectionist that both tracks are in sync.

plug 1. A commercial message slipped into an essentially non-advertising programme, e.g. repeated references to a forthcoming film or deliberate emphasis upon a brand of drink, etc. 2. Electric connector. See **pull plugs**.

Plumbicon A type of camera tube on which the sensitive coating of the target is lead oxide.

pneumatic pedestal A studio camera mounting on which the weight of the camera is balanced by nitrogen gas under pressure. The most common studio pedestal.

point-of-view (POV) Shot simulating the actual viewpoint of a performer as though the viewer were looking through his eyes instead of looking at him. See **subjective filming**.

point-to-point communication satellite A satellite designed to transmit and receive signals from specific locations.

Pola screen (USA) See **polarising filter**.

polar diagram Plot illustrating the directional characteristics of a microphone, loudspeakers or aerial.

polarising filter A filter which polarises light, i.e. causes light waves to vibrate in one phase only, and is used to cut out unwanted reflections from windows, surfaces of swimming pools, etc.

Polaroid 1. The original instant print stills film camera, invented by Dr. Land. Generically used for instant cameras, much used for continuity purposes and checking locations. 2. A plastic material for polarising light. See **polarising filter**.

polecat An adjustable metal beam with spring-loaded ends used for improvising overhead lighting rig on location.

poly (USA = styrofoam) Lighting electricians' abbreviation for **polystyrene**, white, plastic foam sheets used as reflectors.

polygon telecine Flying spot telecine machine that employs a polygonal prism to direct light from a cathode-ray tube on to the photocells through the film. Capable of slow motion and still frame operation.

pop filter (USA) A microphone gag. See **gag**.

pop video The ultimate triumph of form over content.

porch (back porch/front porch) The spaces on the television waveform between the active picture information and the synchronising pulses.

portable single camera (PSC) A British term for single camera work using a video instead of a film camera on location.

portapak Backpack for location portable video recorders.

portaped Lightweight camera pedestal intended for use on location. The weight of the camera is balanced by a column of compressed air, the central column providing the facility to pump itself up to the required pressure.

Portaprompt One type of equipment for projecting a written script on the front of an electronic camera. See **Autocue**.

portholing Fault from electronic cameras in which the image around the edges of the screen appears blurred.

portrait format Composition of a rectangular picture with the longest sides as the verticals. See **landscape format**.

positive/pos 1. The print taken from a negative film, reproducing the tones in the original scene. 2. A voltage above zero (earth) potential.

post-credit sequence Technique mainly seen in feature films where the final action is retained until after the closing credits have been run.

post mortem Post-production editorial meeting to analyse the successes and failures of a show.

post-production The entire sequence of procedures which follow the shooting, specifically editing and dubbing.

post-scoring Writing and performing a background music track after the shooting is completed.

post-sync To add separately recorded dialogue, music or effects after the film has been shot. See **automatic dialogue replacement**.

posterisation Electronic reduction of a picture to a limited number of tones by removing halftones. Common treatment of photographic or film images in graphic sequences.

postiche Theatrical term for wigs, moustaches and false hairpieces.

pot /potentiometer A variable resistor, the wiper or output contact varying between the ends of the resistor.

potter's wheel Reference to the early days of BBC TV when gaps between the transmission of programmes were filled by a film in close up of a pot being thrown on a wheel, or endlessly crashing waves on a shore, or of a tank of tropical fish.

powder down To apply simple studio makeup. Putting on dabs of cosmetic powder to suppress shine from bald heads or sweating faces.

power amplifier High-power amplifier to drive a loudspeaker or the final stage of a transmitter.

power pack Unit for converting AC to DC current and regulating voltages for electronic equipment.

power zoom A zoom lens in which the change of focal length is controlled by an electric motor. Common on video cameras.

practical prop A property which really works used on a set, e.g. a gas cooker, tap, piano, etc.

pre-amplifier An amplifier designed to match a specific low-level source such as a magnetic gramophone pick-up, usually followed by further stages of amplificaton to bring it up to a standard level for conventional amplification.

pre-echo 1. Unwanted interference from adjacent grooves on a disc or from magnetic contamination between adjacent turns on magnetic tape resulting in faint reproduction of sound ahead of its proper time. **2.** Programme planning term to describe the numbers of viewers who turn to a channel early, in anticipation of a particular popular programme.

pre-emphasis The method of pre-distorting the frequency response of a recorder, boosting the high frequencies on recording to improve the overall record/replay performance. Also refers to pre-distortion of the frequency response on transmission to improve reception quality.

pre-fade The method of ensuring that the closing music on a programme finishes on time by running it at a precise moment, but only fading up after the presenter has finished speaking. See **back-timing**.

pre-fade-listen Sound desk facility which enables an incoming sound to be monitored before being faded up. Much used on 'phone-in shows to limit the sudden eruption of obscenity or lunacy on to the airwaves.

pre-mix Sound dubbing technique in which a number of tracks are mixed prior to the final mix.

pre-recorded Recorded before programme transmission.

pre-roll Time required by a projector, telecine or videotape recorder to run up to speed and provide stable pictures and sound.

pre-scoring Composing and performing music prior to filming the action which must then be matched or synchronised to it. See **Mickey Mousing**.

pre-select Function of modern vision mixing and lighting control desks which enables pictures, lighting arrangements, etc, to be set-up prior to them being needed on-air.

pre-selecting/pre-selector The method/combination of buttons, switches and faders, etc, that enables pictures to be set-up prior to being needed on-air.

pre-set and light The complete fitting up of scenery and props and lighting the day or night before a rehearsal or recording.

pre-title sequence Technique of starting a programme by immediately plunging into the action and playing a scene before the opening titles. Particularly common in the USA where the pre-title sequence and opening credits are frequently separated by a commercial break.

première First public showing of a play or film.

prequel The follow-up of a successful drama which is about the younger days of the main characters in the original film.

presence 1. Boosting sound frequencies between 3kHz & 8kHz on replay to make the sound 'brighter' especially in environments where these frequencies are absorbed, e.g. by soft furnishings. Brings sound source subjectively nearer. **2.** The personal charisma of an actor or other performer.

presence filter (USA) See **dialogue equalizer**.

Presentation/Pres Department responsible for linking programmes together and originating trail material for forthcoming programmes.

presentation announcer Presenter, normally out-of-vision, who announces forthcoming programmes during programme junctions.

presentation controller The person who switches from one programme to another and plays in recorded trail material or commercials to ensure the smooth flow of the evening's transmissions. Sometimes the same person as the presentation announcer.

presentation routine The schedule of a day's programmes, including commercials, timings, trails, etc, to be controlled by the presentation controller.

presentation suite/continuity suite The control room, often including sound announcing booth and small studio, through which transmissions are routed.

presenter The compère of a studio, the link man in a magazine show or the in-vision reporter to camera in a documentary.

Pres-fax A BBC system of sending presentation information to the regions using unused lines in the field blanking period of the television signal.

press card Identity card issued by a journalists' union or an employing broadcasting service giving accreditation to a reporter.

press preview/showing Presentation of a programme to an invited audience of journalists prior to public transmission in the hope of eliciting good publicity.

press release An announcement issued to or by the media, either to advertise something or to make a public statement.

presser A news conference. Also loosely used term for any press conference.

pressure pad A component that ensures good contact between magnetic tape and the head in a recorder.

pressure plate Plate in a film camera or projector which holds the back of the film at the precise relationship to the lens.

pressure zone microphone (PZM) Type of microphone, shaped like a tile, which can be placed on floors, walls or desks.

Prestel The British Post Office information system available on a telephone line and connected to a television receiver.

preview A viewing prior to transmission or public theatrical release.

preview monitor Television monitor in the studio gallery where the vision mixer can preview cameras, colour effects, or other sources.

preview theatre Viewing theatre used for press showings, showing commercials to clients, etc.

preview trailer Short extract from a forthcoming programme used for publicity purposes.

Prevost A make of film editing and viewing equipment.

primary colours The three colours from which all other colours in a reproduction system can be produced. In an additive process such as video cameras, the colours are red, green and blue. In a subtractive process such as film, they are yellow, cyan and magenta.

prime lenses Fixed focal length lenses.

Prince of Darkness Derisive term for a studio lighting director or lighting cameraman.

print 1. A positive film derived from a negative. 2. An instruction to a laboratory to process a sequence.

print geometry Description of whether a film has been printed for projection with the emulsion side towards or away from the projector lamp.

print it ! Director's instruction, used mainly on feature films, to announce that an acceptable take has been achieved and should be processed.

print through Fault in tightly wound magnetic tape in which the signal from one layer impresses itself upon an adjacent layer.

print up Optical copying enlargement of a film from a smaller gauge to a bigger one.

printed circuit A copper-clad board on which parts of the copper have been etched away to leave copper strips representing the circuit on to which the components are soldered.

printer 1. The film machine through which the

raw print stock and the processed negative pass
to produce the film print. **2.** A machine that
produces a copy of the information stored in a
computer or a word processor.

printer light Light in a printing machine
giving variable intensity of illumination, used to
grade prints by compensating for differences in
exposure between scenes.

prism Blocks of glass with inclined planes
used to re-direct light by refraction and internal
reflection, used in a range of television
equipment including editing desks and reflex
viewfinders. Electronic cameras contain a prism
to split colours into red, blue and green. See **iceblock**.

prismatic lens A compact form of telephoto
lens.

private automatic branch exchange (PABX)
Automatic internal telephone exchange.

Prix Italia European awards for merit in radio
or television.

process shot **1.** A trick shot in film either by
using special effects or optical printing. **2.** A shot
used as the background to the action in a composite shot. See **matte**.

processing **1.** The chemical process of
developing film. **2.** General term covering
developing, printing, optical titling, etc, carried
out at a film laboratory.

producer Term with a very flexible meaning
depending on context. In USA feature films, the
person who raises and is responsible for money.
In TV, normally the person who launches a
project and has overall responsibility creatively.
In documentary work the producer is often also
the director.

producer's box Sound-proof box containing

output monitors adjacent to the gallery where the producer or guests may observe the recording or transmission of a programme.

production assistant (PA) The person who assists the producer/director in the planning, execution and accounting of a programme and its supporting materials.

production facilities Technical and other back-up resources required to mount a programme.

production manager (PM) In commercial companies often called **1st** or **2nd assistant director**. Responsible to the director for finding and fixing locations, organising rehearsals and planning studio days.

production number An item in a show involving spectacular action and effects usually with a large cast and music. Sarcastically refers to any production activity employing excessive zeal or self-advertisement. See **over the top**.

production secretary Responsible specifically for the clerical and administration work of a production office.

production services manager (PSM) BBC term for the supervisor of the office which allocates camera crews, equipment and cutting rooms to a production. Also known as the **film operations manager (FOM)**.

production unit manager Functionary attached to a film unit mainly concerned with the administration and finances of a shoot.

production values Largely subjective set of cultural and technical merits by which the inherent quality of a programme is judged.

profile flat /piece Two-dimensional cut-out flat used to suggest a silhouette of architectural details, a roofscape, etc.

profile shot Side-view of a performer.

profile spot Lamp using pre-formed cut-outs to project patterns on a cyclorama.

profiles editor Newsroom journalist responsible for keeping and updating biographical details, preparing obituaries, etc.

program interrupt (USA) Term for switched talkback facility in a studio. Sometimes called **interrupted feedback**.

programme 1. A complete, self-contained item in a broadcasting schedule. 2. A set of instructions in the memory of a computer.

programme associate Someone responsible to the producer for financial accounts. A business organiser.

programme -as-brodcast Old name for programme-as-completed.

programme block (USA) **Continuity suite**.

Programme Controllers Group 'Club' of the programme heads of the Big Five British Commercial stations who meet regularly to prepare the network schedules according to their respective strengths. See **Net Advertising Revenue After Levy**.

programme/project number A number given to each programme for library and accounting purposes.

programme prevention officer Derisive term for bureaucratic employees whose function appears to be to create obstacles to programmes happening. Senior equivalent to a **jobsworth**.

programme-as-completed (P-as-C) The document which describes the contents and lists all the financial and legal obligations, e.g. performing rights, repeat fees, etc, made after a programme.

projection booth Soundproof cubicle for film projectors in a cinema or viewing theatre.

projection TV Video display system in which the picture is projected on to a screen and not watched directly on a cathode-ray tube.

projector Device for displaying film, slides or video on to a reflective screen.

promo Promotional recording generally combining pictures on tape or film with a commercial musical recording. See **pop video**.

promotional material Written or other material publicising a programme, film or recording. These may include pens, badges, T-shirts, etc.

PROGRAMME PREVENTION OFFICER

prompt Off-stage or out-of-shot oral reminder to a performer of a script line.

prompt key A defunct method of prompting during live transmission whereby the floor manager could cut studio sound whilst the artist was prompted.

prompter Device for displaying the script in, or close to, the eyeline of a presenter. Trade names include **Autocue**, **Teleprompt**, **Portaprompt**.

properties/props Moveable objects or furniture used to enhance verisimilitude. Divided into the three categories of **action props**, **dressing props** and **personal props**.

property man Operative responsible for looking after props on set or location.

props/properties buyer Person whose job is to obtain props either by hiring from specialist firms or by purchase.

props cage Secure mobile steel cage in which props are stored over-night to prevent them walking off the set.

props plot
1. A floor plan detailing positions of the props on the set.
2. A list of properties required daily.

PRISONER OF ZENDA

PROPS CAGE

proscenium The stage area containing the action, in the theatre often defined and framed by a proscenium arch.

prosthetics Artificial face or body pieces, often constructed from a life cast, used in conjunction with make-up to alter the appearance of a performer.

protagonist The hero or central character in a drama.

protection circuit An additional circuit booked as a back-up on important programmes.

protractor Calibrated, hinged device used to plan angles on floor plans, set designs, etc.

psychodrama Type of dramatic production heavy on introspection and light on storyline. Also, any kind of tantrums or emotional up-heaval amongst members of a production team.

public address (PA) Chain of loudspeakers for addressing a large crowd of people from a central point.

public affairs (USA) See **current affairs**.

Public Broadcasting Services (PBS) (USA) Stations specialising in cultural programmes which are paid for by sponsorship or subscrip-tion, rather than advertising. The main American outlet for British programmes.

public relations (PR) handout Informative publicity material issued or received by a broad-casting organisation.

puddle (USA) To desaturate the colours of a picture to white.

puddling 1. Camera or recording fault causing highlights to appear as blocks of glaring white. 2. Scene painting technique of allowing different tones of wet paint to spread and flow together to break up a surface to suggest crumbling plaster, rising damp, etc.

puff An item in a topical programme which gratuitously gives publicity to a product, event or publication in order to get contributors to the studio. See **plug**.

pull back Dolly a camera backwards.

pull-down Mechanical transport of film through a camera or projector.

pull focus/roll focus Turning the focus ring of a camera to defocus a background and bring the foreground into sharp relief or vice-versa.

pull graphic 1. Remove the top caption on a stand to reveal the next graphic underneath. **2.** To animate mechanically a graphic which has reveals built into it. See **Wurmser**.

pull plugs What may happen if a production tries to exceed the agreed studio or film stage time. The engineers or electricians may then bring the proceedings to a halt by switching off their equipment.

pulling focus Changing focus during a shot to follow a moving object or when the camera itself is dollying. Where focus is critical the assistant cameraman or a special focus puller will help the camera operator.

pulsar Portable quartz spotlight of 650 watts manufactured in Italy.

pulse An electronic signal of finite duration and magnitude used to trigger the scanning system in television, sychronise equipment, etc.

pulse & bar A video test waveform.

pulse code modulation (PCM) Digital encoding system in which each sample of an analogue signal is represented by a digital code.

pulse generator A device that generates pulses of specific duration and frequency. In particular, the device that generates all the different synchronising signals needed in the TV system.

pulse width modulation Digital encodings system in which each sample of an analogue signal is represented by a pulse of variable length.

punch up To select an image by pressing a button on the vision mixing desk, hence the derisive term for a vision mixer 'button puncher'.

punter (*colloq.*) Member of the viewing audience.

pup Small 500 watt spotlight.

puppets Hand-operated models of several types: **1.** Glove puppets. Simple dolls often seen with their operator in vision, mainly on children's programmes. **2.** Hand puppets. A larger (up to man-sized) version of the above, head operated by a main puppeteer but often other operators will work the arms and legs. See **Muppets**. **3.** Rod puppets. All actions are controlled by rods from behind or below. Most large television puppets are a combination of hand and rod techniques. **4.** Marionettes. String operated puppets, often with part of the action animated remotely or by sticks. **5.** Puppets partly remote controlled. See **animatronics**.

push To correct under-exposed film in the film laboratories at the developing stage.

push processing Forced development or cooking the film at the laboratories to increase the apparent sensitivity of under-exposed film.

push-pull-wipe Video digital effect in which one full-frame picture appears to elbow another horizontally out of the screen.

pyrotechnics General term for special effects involving fireworks, explosions and anything combustible in a studio or on location.

python arm Location crane for mounting a hot head camera.

Quad/quadruplex 2-inch wide videotape which uses 4-heads mounted on a wheel to scan the tape transversely. Now largely replaced by later machines using 1-inch and 3/4-inch formats and scan systems.

quad eight 35mm film perforated with five rows of sprocket holes, which can be split after printing into four strips of 8mm film.

quad overlay BBC overlay system, which allows a special effects operator to build up video effects with up to four sources.

quad split Feed of four different picture inputs on to a single screen split into quarters.

quadrophony Four-channel sound recording system.

Quantel Trade name for a manufacturer of sophisticated special effects machines for electronic productions.

quantising levels Discrete steps into which an analogue signal is divided when converting to a digital system.

quarter track A 1/4-inch sound tape recorder with four recording tracks.

quartz light/quartz-halogen light/quartz iodine light A light source using quartz glass and filled with an inert gas and a trace of halogen, usually iodine. More efficient and longer lasting than tungsten lamps, maintaining their correct colour temperature until failure.

question cards Prompt cards of questions or topics held for reference by an interviewer or quizmaster.

RACE See **rapid action cutting equipment.**
RCCB, residual current circuit breaker. See **earth leakage circuit breaker.**

RF See **radio frequency.**

RFI See **radio frequency interference.**

RGB See **red-green-blue.**

RIAA See **Recording Industries Association of America.**

rpm See **revolutions per minute.**

RT See **Radio Times.**

RTS See **Royal Television Society.**

RV See **rendezvous.**

rack 1. Alternative name for the horse or frame from which film is hung into a trim bin. **2.** A frame to which technical equipment is attached.

racking 1. Framing a picture in the gate of a projector. **2.** Metal frame for supporting equipment, films, tapes, etc, general storage. **3.** Sliding trays used for easy withdrawal of equipment from its bays.

racks Technical area in which the irises and colour balances of electronic cameras are remotely regulated and the outputs are matched so that there is no discernible jump when the director cuts from one camera to another. Some functions, such as viewfinder mix, are also controlled from this area.

radiation Strictly any transmitted signal, but usually refers to the undesirable emission of X-rays from very high-voltage circuits and devices.

radio Transmission using electromagnetic waves, usually specifically refers to sound transmission.

radio check An off-air picture from the

transmitter used at an outside broadcast to establish that the output is being transmitted.

radio frequency Any frequency at which electromagnetic signals can be transmitted (generally above 20kHz).

radio frequency interference Unwanted signals picked up on an electronic circuit usually from radio transmissions, police radio signals or unsuppressed vehicle sparking plugs.

radio links Radio signals for relaying sound and picture from an outside broadcast to a studio centre.

radio mike Personal microphone attached to its own portable transmitter which links to a recorder or main studio sound by a radio signal.

radio relay System for transmitting signals over long distances by receiving and then re-transmitting them through a series of relay stations.

Radio Times (RT) Weekly periodical listing all BBC television and radio programmes.

Radiophonic Workshop BBC department which has pioneered the creation of music using synthesized electronic effects.

radiovision An idea for putting television cameras into a radio studio/newsroom, with simultaneous broadcasting on radio and TV. See **simulcast**.

rags Stage curtains parted horizontally rather than raised vertically.

rails Lightweight tracks on which camera dollies can be smoothly manœuvred.

rain deflector A fast-spinning glass disc placed in front of a lens to deflect water splashes.

rain effect Device to sprinkle water on to a window pane simulating rainfall.

rain head High-pressure hosepipe attachment

with adjustable nozzle and deflector used to create artificial rainfall.

rain loop Loop of film or tape superimposed over a scene to give the impression of rainfall. Snow and cloud loops may also be used.

rake The slope from upstage to downstage found in stage theatres.

ramp An inclined rostrum connecting different levels of a set.

random noise Non-repetitive signal on audio or video appearing as 'hiss' on sound or grain on the picture.

Ranks Large British film company founded by J. Arthur Rank, now marketing and producing a wide range of film and electronic equipment as well as processing film for the industry.

rapid action cutting equipment (RACE) Equipment to enable quick cutting between two studio pictures to give a flashing rapid on/off effect.

raster The scanned area, i.e. the area traversed by the beam of electrons across the screen of a picture monitor or receiver. Applied particularly by engineers to a video signal with pulses, but no picture content.

raster graphics A method of displaying graphical data on a television screen.

ratings Estimated comparative audience figures.

ratings war The habit of the different networks of planning their transmission schedules to maximise their own audiences and to capture viewers from the opposition.

ratio See **shooting ratio**.

raunchy Adjective to describe young performers, particularly pop singers, who project an image of aggressive sexuality.

raw stock Unexposed film.

re-broadcast A receiver/transmitter used to pick-up distant transmitters and transmit the received signal to local audiences.

re-established shot A wide-shot re-stating the geography of a situation in a developing scene after a series of close shots or cutaways.

re-position To move a camera, props or backings to the former set-up.

re-record To re-take a shot or scene in studio. Usually implies wiping the original recording.

re-recording room (USA) See **dubbing theatre**.

reach The total number of people who may watch a programme in whole or in part, as distinct from the number of separate receiving sets being watched during a particular show.

reaction shot Rehearsed shot of a performer's physical response to part of the action or a cutaway in unscripted interviews.

read-through The first stage in rehearsal during which the cast simply read aloud their scripts with the director and the writer.

ready 1. A location cameraman's spoken response to a director when he is in a position to start shooting. 2. (USA) PA or director's instruction from the gallery as in *'cam 3 ready!'* i.e. *'coming to camera 3 next.'*

réalisateur French term for a **director**.

realism Style of direction common on TV which uses the techniques of documentary in a fictional context.

rear projection See **back projection**.

recce/reconnaissance A pre-filming visit to a location to work out its suitability, access to facilities, lighting problems, etc.

receiver A device for picking up transmitted signals.

reception The process of receiving transmitted programmes.

reciprocity law Basic law of photography which states that the effect of increased iris and increased exposure time are reciprocal, thus the effect on the film emulsion will be the same for long exposures at small apertures or short exposures at large apertures.

recirculation Replenishment of chemical solutions in the tanks of continuous film processing machines.

reconstruction The use of a dramatic script and actors or models to simulate an event for which actual footage does not exist.

record/recorder/recording Permanent storage medium for electrical signals, e.g. disc or video-tape.

record head Video or sound tape recorder head which records the signal on to passing tape.

record library A library very often containing archive and commercial discs and tapes as well as sound effects.

recorded-as-live Recorded programme, which none the less has been performed in a single continuous take with little or no editing afterwards. Sometimes nonsensically rendered as **live-as-recorded**.

recording break Any interruption to a recording session in a studio either planned or inadvertent.

Recording Industries Association of America (RIAA) Technical standards for recording and replaying magnetic tape sound.

rectifier A device that will pass a current in one direction, only used for converting alternating current into direct current.

red-green-blue (RGB) Simple abbreviation for

the combined three primary colours which make up the television signal.

red light Warning light universally used in film and television studios indicating that filming and recording are taking place.

redhead A small 800 watt portable light used by location units.

reduction print A print of narrower gauge duped from a larger original, e.g. 16mm reduction prints may be made for television transmission from 35mm feature film negatives.

reel (USA) **1**. A spool. **2**. A cut roll of film, usually a complete item or programme.

reel-to-reel System of spooling video or sound tape from one open spool to another past the record or playback heads, as opposed to a cassette system.

reference black level The signal level of a TV picture which is always the darkest part of the picture.

reflectance The percentage of incident light reflected by a surface.

reflected light Description of the measurable light reflected from a surface as distinct from the incident light, which is the measure of the intensity of light emitted by a light source.

reflector A piece of reflective material either specially constructed or improvised from aluminium foil or white polystyrene (USA styrofoam), which is used on location instead of a battery light to reflect sunlight on to a close-up shot and to provide soft lighting for studio shots.

reflex camera A film or stills camera in which the viewfinder image is obtained through the objective lens, i.e. precisely the same image as on the film. See **reflex shutter**.

reflex projection See **axial front projection**.

reflex shutter Shutter which both obscures the film as it is pulled down and forms an image on ground glass which is passed prismatically to the viewfinder.

reflex viewfinder Camera viewfinder which uses a prism and mirror system to look directly through the lens of a camera.

refractive index A measure of the amount that light which is bent (refracted) when it passes from a less dense to a more dense medium, or vice versa. The effect can be seen by placing a garden cane in a bucket of water where the cane appears to bend at the surface of the water.

register 1. To place in exact position or alignment. 2. To ensure precise superimposition of the individual red, blue and green images from the three tubes of a video camera.

register pin See **pin registration**.

registration Positioning of one frame after another in a camera or projector. The smallest variation will cause a jump or blur.

rehearsal A practice session running through the action before a recording or transmission. See **camera rehearsal**.

rehearsal rooms Rooms furnished with basic props and marked up to show the position of scenery, etc, used for rehearsals by a production before going into the studio or on location.

rehearsal script The first working script in a production involving dialogue and stage instructions, but without any technical instructions which are later incorporated on a studio or shooting script.

rehearse/record Discontinuous recording of scenes in an electronic studio.

Reithian A disciple of Lord Reith, first Director General of the BBC, who believed in

the concept of an impartial and comprehensive
public broadcasting service whose main duty
was to serve all sectors and tastes without
concern for commercial or political advantage
while refusing to allow lowest common
denominator programming in pursuit of a
maximum audience.

relay 1. An electronically-controlled mechanical switch. **2.** Transmission of signals by radio links.

relay station A complex that receives
television or radio signals and re-transmits them.
Needed particularly in mountainous districts
where there are reception difficulties, or to boost
signals over long distances.

release camera one/ two/ three! Director's
instruction that a studio camera is finished with
in one scene and should move to its next position.

release print
Print available
for public viewing
whilst the original
is kept in safety
in a film unit.

Rembrandt
*Every frame
a Rembrandt*':
derisive description
of film camera-
work which is too
artful and pretty
for its own good.

REMBRANDT

Rembrandt lighting Dramatic use of chiaroscuro effect in film or studio lighting.

remote (USA) A multi-camera outside broadcast.

remote camera A camera on an outside broadcast, usually called a 'remote', separated from the other cameras and control room by a considerable distance, often linked by radio to the control room especially if mounted on a vehicle, boat, etc.

remote control The setting up or controlling of equipment at a distance by cable, radio, infra-red or other means.

remote pickup A distant camera or microphone, usually connected to the mixing point by radio link.

remote source (USA) Term for any external input into a television studio gallery.

rendezvous (RV) Scheduled meeting place and time issued to a location team by the production assistant.

repeat The second or subsequent showing of a recorded programme. Particularly prevalent during public holiday periods and times of financial stringency, occasionally also reflecting the excellence of a production.

repeat fee Fee paid to a contracted artist based on a proportion of the original performance fee as payment for repeats of a programme.

repeater An unattended receiver/transmitter for boosting signals.

répétiteur 1. A prompt. 2. In major orchestral or choral events, an assistant conductor who relays the main conductor's instructions and timings to performers unable to see him/her, e.g. if orchestra and singers are in different studios. Uses a monitor to take cues from the main conductor. **3.** In opera and ballet, a person who conducts rehearsals, concentrating on technical rather than creative content, up to the point where the artistic director comes in.

replay (USA) See **playback**.

reporter A presenter/summariser; someone on a topical programme, usually a journalist, who is interposed between the camera and the subject.

Representation of the People Act Legislation which, amongst other things, ensures regulation of airtime available to political parties.

reproduction Playback of a recorded signal.

requisition form Order by a production department for a service within a studio, such as scene painting, camera crewing, special effects, etc.

researcher Member of the production team whose main function is to investigate subjects, collate background information and recce likely locations for future programmes.

reset To restore a piece of equipment or an item on a set to its original condition or position.

residuals Payments to writers and performers for sales and other commercial exploitation of a film or programme.

resin box Box of powdered resin into which dancers dip their shoes to avoid slipping.

resolution The degree to which fine detail in a picture may be distinguished, normally dependent on lens quality and the grain of the film emulsion.

resolving power A measure of the ability of an electronic system to 'see' detail.

resonance Oscillation of a piece of mechanical or electrical equipment at its natural frequency.

resting Actors' euphemism for being unemployed.

retakes Similar shots repeated a number of times to achieve a satisfactory result or to give a number of alternatives to a film or VT editor.

reticulation A wrinkling effect on the emulsion of film caused by careless storage or faulty processing.

return Right-angled extension to a run of flattage to prevent a camera shooting off or the audience seeing the end of the set.

return feed When a TV interview is carried out with the interviewer in a remote studio, the main studio output is fed back to him or her so both protagonists can see and hear one another.

Reuters International news gathering agency servicing both newspaper and television journalism.

revamp To paint or modify a stock set in order to make it usable for a different production. (USA) Re-edit of news footage between bulletins.

reveal 1. Narrow stage flattage at 90 degrees used in doorways, etc, to simulate depth or thickness. **2.** The emergence of one picture from another, e.g. by a wipe. **3.** Type of simple animated card caption in which sliding black card is manipulated in vision to reveal or conceal parts of the information on a card beneath. See **Wurmser**.

reverb Abbreviation for **sound reverberation**.

reverberation time The time taken for a sound to die away or decay depending on the acoustic of an enclosed space. More precisely the time taken for a sound to fall in level by 60dB after cessation of the direct sound.

reverberation unit/chamber Device for creating echo effects.

reversal film Film which, when processed, produces a positive image which is therefore the unique copy. Used for colour slides but usually only for amateur or news purposes on moving film.

reversal original The processed original film stock that directly produces a positive image when processed and which is therefore the master.

reverse/reverse angle In a dialogue or interview sequence where only one camera is used, a shot in which the second performer or interviewer repeats lines or questions so that both sides of the conversation can subsequently be cut together smoothly.

reverse motion Effect achieved either by filming with the camera upside down or by laboratory printing to reverse ordinary action, e.g. a demolished chimney suddenly re-erecting

REVERSE MOTION

itself. Used for trick violent effects like a thrown knife narrowly missing the hero. In reality, the knife starts in the door and is pulled out and the shot subsequently printed backwards. Easily achieved as a videotape effect on professional machines.

reverse phase 1. Electronic means of turning black and white film negative into a positive image on transmission without having to make a print. **2.** To reverse the polarity of an audio lead to ensure that two or more microphones reinforce rather than cancel each other.

reverse scan Electronic trick for flipping a picture to give a mirror image of the original.

reverse vision circuit A vision feed sent back from base to an outside broadcast often used in association with clean feed sound circuit.

revolutions per minute (rpm) Description of the speed of rotation of a record disc.

revolve 1. A rotating circular platform consisting of concentric rings built into a theatre stage. **2.** Rewind to transport film or tape back on to its feed spool.

rewind bench Cutting room bench with geared flywheels on which film rolls may be fast rewound.

rhubarb Term given to meaningless background speech in a crowd scene; the muttering of extras.

ribbon microphone A high-quality microphone which generates an electrical signal from a fine metal strip made to vibrate within a magnetic field by the variations of air pressure caused by sound waves.

riff Jazz/pop term for a musical phrase regularly repeated.

rifle mike Highly-directional microphone

favoured by film sound recordists for covering dialogue and interviews on location, also called a **gun mike**.

rig/de-rig Putting up or striking scenery, sound equipment and lights.

rigger Operative responsible for the physical installation of cameras, cables, scaffolding, etc, at an outside broadcast. A rigger driver has further responsibility for the OB vehicles.

rigging crew Location technical team who go ahead of a travelling roadshow to prepare sets.

rim light Back light used to emphasise the separation of head and shoulders from the background.

ring main Cable system for distributing transmissions and studio outputs around offices, etc.

ring modulator See **audio modulator**.

ring steer A ring fitted below the camera head which allows the pedestal to be steered in any direction.

ringing Video aberration appearing after a sudden change in brightness in which the outlines of subjects appear briefly ringed by oscillating light.

rip-and-read Newsroom term for a news agency teleprinter. The sheets torn from it are called **rips**.

ripple 1. Regular wavering of the picture from side-to-side causing a wavy effect to run vertically down the picture. An early technique to suggest a jump in time. **2.** Simulated effect of rippling water from an attachment to a luminaire. **3.** Unwanted AC on a DC supply.

ripple dissolve/wipe A combination of a ripple effect and a mix or wipe to another shot. An out-dated convention for implying the beginning or end of a dream sequence.

ripple trough A black-bottomed tray filled with water to which fragments of broken mirror are added. To achieve a ripple effect, a light is shone at an angle and the resulting rippling shadows and reflected highlights are bounced on to the action.

rise An actor's move from a sitting to a standing position.

riser Rostrum used to create a step on the set.

road film Fashion in films of the 1960's in which the action follows the adventures of characters in transit from one location to another, e.g. *Easy Rider*.

road show An outside broadcast series in which successive episodes come from different locations.

roadie Road agent/manager, a person who works with a travelling musical group fixing accommodation, installation of technical equipment, lighting, etc.

rock and roll Film dubbing system where picture and sound tracks may be run backwards or forwards independently of each other.

rock focus Effect achieved by throwing the lens focus ring back and forth. Used for effect in pop music videos or to suggest disorientation or intoxication in a subjective camera shot.

roll 1. A roll of film or tape. 2. (USA) Director's instruction for a camera to turn over. 3. Fault in a TV picture causing the image to rotate vertically through the screen.

roll bar Fault caused by imperfect synchronisation when the black bar between film or videotape frames becomes visible on the TV screen. Appears as a dark bar which rolls up or down the screen.

roll focus (USA) Pulling focus in shot.

roller caption Caption commonly used for end credits. Sometimes printed on a long roll of black card or else electronically generated. The credits are made to appear to run through frame vertically or horizontally.

roller prompter (USA) See **prompter**.

rollerball (USA) Joystick control for a camera.

rolling legs/tripod A spreader mounted on wheels used to convert a tripod into a simple camera dolly.

rolling title (USA) See **roller caption**.

room sound The natural acoustic of an interior.

rostrum Box-like structure used to raise the ground level of a theatre or studio set.

rostrum camera Film/video camera mounted over a moveable bench upon which still pictures can be animated.

rotoscope A system for exactly matching live action and graphics. The artist traces artwork from projected frames of live action film.

rough cut The end of the first creative stage of editing in which all the main sequences have been roughly assembled in order.

routeing The direction of electronic sources to destinations.

routine 1. A dance number. 2. A short programme sequence that may be repeated.

roving eye A mobile video camera platform radio-linked back to its base, e.g. much used in horse-racing to keep abreast of the horses .

roving spot Hand-operated spotlight mounted on a pivoting head used in the theatre and television to follow a performer. Also called **follow spot**.

row A low flat cutout running along the bottom of a run of flats or a backcloth to conceal ground row lighting.

Royal Television Society (RTS) British professional association for broadcasters and engineers.

royalty 1. Commission fee paid to authors and composers, as copyright. **2.** Essential member of audience at annual British variety performance.

rubber numbers System of matching numbers printed in ink along the edge of film, sound and picture tracks to aid the editor to locate and match trims.

rubdown (USA) See **Letraset**.

rule of thirds Guide to scenic composition which states that a pleasing result is achieved if the screen is divided into nine squares by three imaginary, equally spaced, vertical lines and three horizontal ones. The optimum points of interest will be the points of intersection.

rumble Very low-frequency noise associated with poor quality or damaged disc turntables.

rumble filter Sometimes in a dubbing theatre called **hum filter**. Equipment for cutting out undesired low-frequency sounds.

run 1. The length of time a play stays in continuous production or a TV series is transmitted. **2.** A line of scenery flats simulating a continuous wall, etc. **3.** A length of cable. **4.** Command given by a gallery director to start videotape or telecine machine.

run down A quick resumé of programme content or sequence of action.

run through Rehearsal of a complete show with only minimal interruption.

run to record Instruction by technical co-ordinator or studio director to VT to start the machine and get up to operational speed prior to recording a take.

run- up time Time taken for mechanical

equipment to get up to the correct operational speed, e.g. videotape recorders.

runner 1. A topical story which will recur regularly over a succession of bulletins or weeks enabling updates to be made, e.g. a lengthy court case or a long strike. **2.** Most junior operative on a feature film set. See **gofer**

running Verbal announcement by a sound recordist to the film director and cameraman or by the cameraman to the director that they have heard the instruction '*turnover*!' and their equipment is operating; recordists often use the alternative word '*speed*!'. Only after this confirmation will the director call '*action*!' for a scene to begin.

running gag Recognisable joke or comic situation which is repeated during a programme or throughout a light entertainment series.

running order A schedule for a magazine programme showing the sequence of items, durations and content.

running speed Rate at which a film passes through a camera or projector, or tape through a recorder.

running time Length of transmission from beginning to end of a film or television programme.

rush prints/rushes The film, picture and sound as returned by the film laboratory and film sound transfer suite in their unedited state for viewing and synchronisation.

rust The iron-oxide coating of magnetic tape compared jokingly to the silver which is the basis for a film emulsion.

Ryley A make of caption generator used for opening and closing titles and name captions, e.g. sub-titling, etc.

S B See **simultaneous broadcast.**

S4C See **Sianel Pedwar Cymru.**

SFX Script abbreviation for **sound effects.**

SHF See **super high frequency.**

S/I Script abbreviation for **superimpose.**

SIS See **sound in syncs.**

SKC See **Service Kinematographic Company.**

SLR See **single-lens reflex.**

SMATV See **Satellite Master Antenna Television.**

SMPTE See **Society of Motion Picture & Television Engineers.**

SMPTE leader Type of leader spliced on the beginning of a film prior to projection, both to protect the film and to enable sound and picture tracks to be synchronised.

S/N See **signal to noise ratio.**

SOF Script abbreviation for **sound on film.**

SOT/SOVT Script abbreviations for **sound on tape/sound on videotape.**

SOV See **sound on vision.**

SPG See **synchronising pulse generator.**

SR Abbreviation for **silent reflex.** 16mm Arriflex camera.

SSVC See **Services Sound & Vision Corporation.**

STV See **Scottish Television.**

SUM See **Sony U-matic videotape.**

SUP Abbreviation for **shot under protest.**

Safari Citroën Safari car used for a roving eye camera mounting.

safe area Area of the picture composition least likely to be cut off by ill-adjusted domestic receivers. See **cut off, overscanning.**

safe light Light used in a dark room using only the colours of the spectrum to which the emulsion of the film being used is insensitive, usually red or green.

safety film/base Old term to distinguish film manufactured with a plastic base instead of the original nitrate stock which was dangerously unstable.

safety officer Official employed to ensure that the requirements of the health and safety legislation are observed and for advising on safety harnesses, security of camera positions, etc, on location.

safety shot 1. General covering shot containing the whole continuous action of a drama scene to cover subsequent failures in direction or performance. **2.** Current affairs term for a shot of no specific utility, which might come in handy later in the cutting room when the director decides what he is doing.

Sam Major Large camera crane with a hydraulic centre column.

sample print (USA) See **answer print**.

Samuelson's (*colloq.* **Sammie's**) A leading British equipment rental company.

sand bag Canvas bag filled with sand used as a simple stage weight or counterweight for suspended scenery.

satellite 1. A solar-powered receiver/transmitter in orbit around the earth. **2.** A sub-station associated with a main station.

Satellite Master Antenna Television (SMATV) System whereby programmes relayed via satellite or received by a dish aerial are then redistributed to domestic receivers by a cable system.

satellite station A ground station for transmitting to, and receiving from, satellites.

Saticon Type of video tube widely used in

industrial cameras using selenium arsenic tellurium in its photosensitive surface and giving better resolution than Vidicon tubes.

saturated colour Pure colour containing no white.

saturation The degree of purity of a colour, i.e. its freedom from dilution by white.

saturation lighting Method of arranging studio lights so that every area of a studio has sufficient lights already available (usually dual source types) so as to avoid the need to rig each light specially for each job.

sawtooth Test signal consisting of a continuous transition from black to white across the screen with a rapid return to black before the next line commences. It resembles a sawtooth shape when displayed on an oscilloscope.

scan The build-up of a picture master on a television screen.

scan burn Mark left on CRT by continuous use at high brightness (usually in the shape of the scan or raster).

scan reversal The ability to reverse a picture either vertically or horizontally on a camera or monitor.

scanner General term for mobile control rooms in an outside broadcast.

scenario **1.** A film screenplay. **2.** Outline of situation or film story.

scene **1.** Sync system for linking the panning movement of a background camera in a chromakey sequence with the foreground camera, so synchronising the appropriate movements. **2.** Section of a film or theatrical performance with action taking place continuously on one location at a single time.

scene dock The area adjacent to a stage or

studio where scenery and props are temporarily stored.

scene hoist Tackle by which drapes, flats, etc, can be flown up to the grid.

scenemaster Foreman in charge of scheduling scenic construction, servicing, painting and striking of sets.

scenery Solid sets constructed to give the illusion of locations in a studio or on a stage.

scenic artist Artist working to the designer who paints special backdrops or detailed work upon scenery.

scenic effect A special effect that takes place as part of the live action on stage rather than created electronically in post production.

scenic painting Painting of backdrops and detail on scenery, or specialist work on glass for film glass shots.

scenic projection General term for the various ways in which a set is created by projecting a photographic image to appear behind the actors. See **axial front projection, Eidophor.**

schlock Films or programmes calculated to get a maximum lowest common denominator audience by exploiting sex, violence, fantasy or any currently fashionable trend. Hence **schlockmeister**, a producer specialising in corn and tat.

Schools Broadcasting Educational programmes devised to enhance school curricula.

Schwem Manufacturers of gyroscopically-stabilised zoom lens and other optical equipment.

scoop 1. An exclusive news story. 2. To get a story out before anyone else. 3. A large, old-fashioned, soft light.

Scoopic Small, mute film camera.

scope 1. An oscilloscope. 2. Cinemascope film format.

score Musical composition written as an accompaniment to a programme or film and used to heighten the dramatic mood.

scoring stage Theatre in which the picture is projected before an orchestra, who perform the score in synchronism with the action.

Scotchlight screen Screen used for front axial projection on a film stage.

Scottish Television (STV) IBA company serving the Lowlands and west coast of Scotland.

scrambled/scrambling A means of transmission where the information is deliberately mixed up so that the viewer/listener needs a special decoder to receive the programme, usually in return for a fee.

scratch commentary Rough outline commentary used for judging cues and timing by a film or tape editor prior to a proper dub.

scratch copy A print sent out for viewing or papering up purposes only, which has been deliberately scratched along the middle to prevent unauthorised use.

scratch filter Apparatus in a sound dubbing theatre to cut out unwanted high-frequency sounds.

scratch pad Computer control pad operated either by keyboard touch or light pen.

scratch print A rough contact print taken from a completed cutting copy usually for use in the dubbing theatre.

scratch video Juxtaposition of images and clips from mainstream film and television set to pop music either for political purposes or to make connections and meanings undreamed of by the original film-makers.

scratches Scored lines on film negative or print caused by mechanical damage in the film transport or dirt in the camera gate or laboratory processing machines.

screeded floor A floor laid to precise studio standards, so that tracking shots are smooth.

screen 1. To arrange a film viewing. 2. The special reflective material on to which pictures are projected. 3. A conducting surface which prevents ingress of electrical or magnetic interference.

Screen Advertising World Association Main association of television and film commercial makers and organiser of an annual Film Festival.

screen credit Printed acknowledgement appearing at the beginning or end of a film listing participants in the production.

screen direction Film direction, the overall control of the action and shooting of a film.

screen mask Border placed around the projected image area of a screen as a picture frame.

screen test Feature film term for an audition; generally done before a camera.

screen writer Feature film term for the person who writes an original screenplay or adapts other work for screen purposes.

screened cable/head Cable surrounded by a metal braided sheath that acts as mechanical protection and an electrostatic shield. See **co-axial cable**.

screening A showing of a programme for preview or critical purposes.

screenplay A script prepared by a writer which includes indications of shots and actions and is the basis for any feature film production.

screwball comedy (USA) School of farce combining juvenile slapstick with winsomeness.

scrim Gauze material put in front of a lamp or

window to diffuse and soften the light or to protect a bare bulb.

script 1. The words of a commentary or performance. 2. The detailed scene-by-scene instructions for a film or TV production including action, dialogue and camera instructions in specialised forms, e.g. a shooting script, cutting script, etc.

script assistant (USA) Film continuity girl or TV production assistant. Hence French for a PA, **La Script**.

script editor 1. A person who adapts an original screenplay to a particular programme need. 2. Assistant to a producer in a television series who ensures consistency of characterisation, storyline, continuing sub-plots, etc, when a team of writers is employed.

scumbling Applying translucent layer of paint over a textured surface on scenery.

search Ability of videotape players to run quickly backwards and forwards without losing the picture on the monitor.

SECAM (*Sequential Couleur à Memoire*) 625-line system of television developed in France. See also **PAL, NTSC**.

second clap Instruction by cameraman to his assistant telling him at the beginning of a take that the clapperboard was not clearly visible. The camera is kept running and the board shown again with a verbal identification, e.g. *'scene one, take two, sync to second clap!'*.

second eye The use of the opinion of a superior or an outside party to give a critical analysis of a programme in an unfinished state, usually a rough cut in the cutting room or VT edit suite.

second generation A recording dubbed from one tape to another, subsequently third, fourth, fifth generations, each one increasingly losing quality. This will not be so with the advent of digital recorders.

Second Law of Television Generally expressed as *'never be unkind to people when you're on the way up, as you're going to meet them again on the way down.'*. See also **Murphy's Law**.

second unit Camera crew led by an assistant director who films background shots, action scenes or trick sequences, whilst the director of the principal unit concentrates on the main action.

secondary colours Colours formed by a mixture of two of the three primary broadcasting colours; red, blue and green.

sector chart (USA) See **pie chart**.

Segué/Seguay (pronounced SEGWAY) To run one piece of music directly into another without pausing. Probable origin *sigue*, Spanish, go on, follow, continue.

Selecta Vision Trade name for an interactive videodisc system.

self-blimped A film camera requiring no extra sound proofing because of its inherently quiet operation.

semi-scripted A show in which the opening and closing are rigidly controlled and the structure is defined, but the main part is impromptu, e.g. chat shows, quizzes.

semiology The study of semiotics.

semiotics Academic school of criticism which analyses the structures of symbolic verbal and non-verbal communication in films, e.g. why good cowboys wear white hats and bad cowboys black ones. Not much use to real film makers.

send up To parody or satirise the performance

Sennheiser A popular range of microphones made in Austria.

sensitivity 1. Minimum usable input for a receiver. **2.** The speed of a film emulsion.

sensitometer Film laboratory instrument for analysing emulsions and testing their response to processing.

sensitometric strip A strip of film (or on the edge of a photographic print) given different exposures to determine the optimum setting.

sensitometry The study of the sensitivity of photographic materials to light and relationship between exposure and density after processing.

separation light Alternative name for a back light on an artist, which appears to throw the background set away from him by emphasising the gap between the two.

separation negative A one-colour negative in the Technicolor process — black and white negatives from red/blue/green.

sepmag (separate magnetic) Normal system for editing and showing film on TV. The sound track is kept separately on magnetic film of the same mechanical dimensions as the picture, as opposed to being physically combined with the picture as in **commag** or **comopt prints.**

sepopt (separate optical) Early system of film sound reproduction in which a separate optically printed sound track is run in synchronism with the picture.

sequel Production picking up the continuing plot and characters of an earlier successful film or series. See also **prequel.**

sequence Series of shots put together to make a self-contained section of a larger programme.

serial A continuous dramatic story broken into a number of episodes transmitted at intervals.

series A number of programmes transmitted at regular intervals which share the same basic cast and situation, but where a self-contained story is told in each episode.

Services Kinematographic Company (SKC) Film making arm of the British Armed Forces, now amalgamated with BFBS into SSVC.

Services Sound & Vision Corporation (SSVC) Film and broadcasting organisation of the British Armed Forces incorporating the Services Kinematograph Corporation and the British Forces Broadcasting Service.

servo-controlled A remote, positional control for a number of devices, e.g. zoom lenses.

servo-system Electro-mechanical circuits used in VTRs to lock the videoheads to the signal either being recorded or replayed.

session man/player A musician who performs anonymously on an *ad hoc* basis to record backing tracks, mood music, discs, etc.

set The scenery complete with furniture and props in which the action takes place.

set and light Time before shooting in a studio when sets are erected and lighting is adjusted.

set clamp A clamp to hold two flats together or to allow a lamp to be mounted on the set itself.

set designer Designer responsible for the architectural element of the design.

set dressing The process whereby the designer embellishes the basic scenery by adding setting props. See **dressing props**.

set in To put dressing properties or scenery in a set to improve shot composition or add to the design ready for a shot. Opposite to **strike** properties.

set jack (USA) **Gaffer**. In charge of scenic servicing and rigging lights.

set light 1. Lighting to illuminate and enhance the set design as distinct from the action. 2. A fixed setting of lighting dimmers that make a useful starting position before a lighting balance is carried out.

set up 1. Time taken to erect and dress a set. 2. Position of a camera in relation to the scene or subject. 3. The amount above which the reference level picture black is set. See **pedestal (electronic)**.

setting Erecting and decorating a stage set.

setting floor Workshop area where sets are assembled for painting.

setting props Properties used to embellish a constructed set, e.g. small items of furniture, pictures, flowers, etc, as distinct from action props which are properties handled by actors as part of the plot, e.g. weapons, watches, cigarette lighters, etc.

sex changer A connector for joining together cables ending with two male or two female plugs.

sexploitation movie Indifferent film selling on its reputation for salacious or pornographic elements.

shading A fault in an ageing camera tube or the result of faulty electronics or poor line-up that results in a variable colour cast across the picture.

shadow mask A type of colour display tube which has a perforated metal screen through which the electron beams are directed on to the phosphor dots.

shallow focus shot Technique of isolating a subject from its surroundings by focusing so that it alone is sharp, and foreground or background parts of the composition are an indistinct blur.

sharp In focus.

shash Snowstorm effect on a TV screen caused by a faulty signal or failure of the aerial.

Sheffield plate Outside broadcast camera mounting, so called because developed for use at Sheffield Wednesday football ground.

shelf item A news or magazine item lacking any specific, topical peg which may therefore be held in reserve to fill a gap in a programme. See **standby**.

shift The controls for moving the relative horizontal or vertical of the red, green and blue images so that they are exactly superimposed. Adjustments are available on cameras and monitor/receivers.

shim Piece of metal used to space any other two pieces of metal.

shoot Generic term for a specific filming or recording project.

shooting off Composing a shot in which the scenery is not contained and studio walls, other sets, or a bare cyclorama are revealed.

shooting order The order in which a programme is to be shot, not necessarily the order in which it will appear on the screen after editing.

shooting ratio The ratio of film footage shot to the amount needed for the final print, e.g. eight hours of actual shot film cut down to a one-hour show would be represented as a ratio of eight-to-one.

shooting schedule Detailed timetable prepared from a shooting script giving times, locations, rendezvous, etc, for all members of a production.

shooting script Detailed breakdown of a script listing the shots to be done and the sequence in which they are to be filmed.

short A film made for theatrical distribution of

half-an-hour or less duration and traditionally accompanying A and B feature films in a cinema programme.

short circuit Fault in wiring allowing an electrical current to escape without going through the resistance of the intended circuit.

short focal length lens A lens with a wide-angle field of view.

shot An unedited action or part of a scene or sequence. A take; the basic subdivision of a film.

shot box A box of switches attached to an OB or studio camera from which a selection of lenses may be instantly selected, enabling a zoom lens to be operated in the same way as a turret.

shot calling In a studio gallery one of the jobs of the production assistant, who calls out the number of each shot listed on the camera script as it comes up and also announces the source, (e.g. TK, VT, another camera) of the next shot.

shot list List of camera shots written down by the production assistant on location noting the content and duration for subsequent reference by the director and film editor.

shot number On a programme script each shot is numbered to ensure that everyone concerned knows which point the recording/transmission has reached.

shot plotter (USA) See **protractor**.

shot-by-shot approach Filming organised to minimise editing by planning and shooting each scene in sequence as it will finally appear. Mainly used by home video makers.

shotgun (USA) A highly directional rifle mike.

shoulder pod Attachment to the camera body enabling the cameraman to rest it firmly on his shoulder during lengthy hand-held sequences.

show A theatrical production. In TV parlance,

usually used in terms of an audience participation production centred upon a TV personality, e.g *The Johnny Carson Show*, etc.

show copy Positive print of a completed film used for preview purposes or première.

show print The final print of a film programme accepted from the laboratories by the director; also known as the **transmission** or **TX print**.

show reel Assembly reel of film or tape compiled by a director or cameraman as an example of work to show to prospective employers.

showbiz (USA) Generic term for the light entertainment industry, in film, television, stage and variety.

shutter A device to cut off light in an optical instrument, e.g. the mechanism on a camera which exposes each frame of film by opening and shutting, or the interruption of the light source from a projector by a rotating blade whilst film pull-down occurs.

shuttle Fast forward or backward motion of a videotape or telecine whilst the picture remains visible. In a cassette machine, the videotape has therefore to remain laced in 'shuttle'.

Sianel Pedwar Cymru (S4C) Welsh language Channel Four showing programmes generated by BBC Wales, Harlech TV and independent producers.

sig. tune /signature tune An easily recognisable passage of music used to introduce and close a regular programme.

Sight & Sound Magazine of the British Film Institute which is read by film **buffs**. See **semiotics**.

signal to noise ratio (S/N) Level of signal with respect to unwanted electronic noise present in all audio/video apparatus.

signposting Inserting references in the opening headline sequence or in a link in the middle of a magazine programme to remind the viewer what is coming next.

silent camera Camera without capacity for recording sound.

silent cinema Films shot without sound.

silhouette shot Shot of a person lit only by the backlight. Used for dramatic effect or to conceal identity.

sill iron Strip of metal across the bottom of a doorway or french window which acts as a brace.

silly season Description of summer months when Parliament is in recess and most of the journalists are on holiday. Silly or inconsequential news stories often run at this time.

silver recovery 1. Process by which unexposed silver halide is removed from a film emulsion during the fixing stage of the process. **2.** Means of retrieving the silver from the chemical solution in continuous processing machines.

Simon hoist A tall crane used as a camera platform for very high-angle shots; also known as a **cherry picker**.

simulcast Simultaneous transmission of television and stereo radio programmes, typically of a live concert or opera.

simultaneous broadcast (SB) When two stations simultaneously take a broadcast item generated from one or the other, but link in and out of their individual programmes separately.

single camera shooting Normal film shooting technique used on location in film or video. As only one camera is used, even on simple set ups like an interview, everything has to be shot out-of-sequence, e.g. answers first and questions second, then edited together to create the illusion of continuity.

single frame/single frame exposure Animation techniques in which frames are exposed one at a time whilst artwork or models are adjusted between exposures. See **rostrum camera, stop frame**

single light print An ungraded print of a film run off at a single exposure used for slash prints, ungraded rushes, etc.

single shot 1. A close shot distinguishing one person from a group. 2. Exposing a film one frame at a time, e.g. in animation.

single standard A piece of equipment capable of working in only one television standard, PAL, NTSC or SECAM.

single system Film system in which sound and pictures are recorded simultaneously on the same length of film or tape. See **commag**.

single-clad Scenery, usually **flattage**, designed to be seen only from the front.

single-lens reflex (SLR) Camera in which the viewfinder looks directly through the camera lens via a system of prisms and mirrors.

single-phase A mains power source requiring connections to equipment designed to be operated with connections to one live wire and the neutral.

sit 1. An actor's movement from a standing to a sitting position. 2. Electronic control of the picture black level.

sitcom/situation comedy A drama series, usually with a regular cast, set in a domestic situation where the comedy comes from variations on a single theme. Normally transmitted as a finite series of mini-plays, as opposed to a soap opera which is essentially interminable. Almost always performed before a studio audience but sometimes with additional recorded applause, laughter, etc, added.

six-plate A film editing table which is capable of playing two separate magnetic sound tracks synchronised to the picture.

six-two-five 625-line system on PAL or SECAM usual in colour transmission worldwide, except in America and Japan which use a 525-line, NTSC system.

sixteen millimetre (16mm) Commonest television film gauge, having largely supplanted thirty-five millimetre for economy reasons.

size of shot Description of how much of a person appears in vision, e.g. mid-shot, etc.

skate (USA) A wheeled spider at the base of **rolling legs**.

skateboarding duck A supposedly topical story of a silliness obvious to everyone but the perpetrator. Refers to a famous item in the BBC Current Affairs magazine programme *Nationwide* featuring a duck on a skateboard which was subsequently widely satirised.

skew Picture distortion where verticals are not at right angles to horizontals. May be the result of mechanical defects or adjustments, e.g. tape tension in a replay VTR.

skid A flat, wheeled platform for a tripod. See **spider, skate**.

skid dolly (USA) See **spider, rolling legs**.

skinflick A film with overtly pornographic content.

skip Large container for costumes or props, traditionally of basketwork.

skip framing (USA) Also known as **step printing**, but specifically when every second or third frame of a film is printed to speed up the action.

sky/sky boom! Instruction by a director to a boom operator to raise a microphone which has dropped into shot.

Sky Channel British satellite and cable broadcasting company.

sky cloth A stretched blue or white backcloth which can be lit to suggest the sky.

sky filter Graduated light filter used to darken the clear blue sky without affecting the rest of the scene.

slant Editorial content or bias.

slant track Obsolete format for videotape machines replaced by helical scan format.

SKATEBOARDING DUCK

slap Slang term for make-up.

slapstick Knockabout farce involving implied physical violence, so-called because of using two planks of wood 'slapsticks' to produce simple instant sound effects in the theatre. The basic format for silent cinema comedy.

slash drapes Curtains of reflective silvered material, slashed into narrow strips and used on light entertainment shows.

slash print A film print taken directly off an existing print rather than via negative. Used when quality is unimportant, e.g. to duplicate a cutting copy with so many joins that it would be unreliable on projection at a dubbing session.

slate Usual familiar term for a clapperboard with information such as title, scene and take number on it or for a shot number. See **board**.

slate it! Instruction to put the clapperboard into shot to identify it.

slave The control of one piece of equipment from another, e.g. a remote pulse generator, or timecode generator controlled from a local generator to ensure synchronisation.

slave unit A remote device controlled from a master unit.

slavelock The locking of a remote pulse generator to the local or master generator. Reverse of **genlock**.

slide A still photographic transparency used for projection.

slide chain Alternative name for caption scanner. A fixed electronic camera used for transmitting transparencies.

slide file (Rank/Cintel slide file) Means of electronically storing video frames, now replacing the telejector system. See **picture grabbing**, **art file**.

slide projector A machine for projecting transparencies.

slide scanner Alternative name for caption scanner. A fixed electronic camera used for transmitting transparencies.

Slingsby A kind of two-wheeled trolley used manually to transport heavy equipment.

slipping sync Also known as **creeping sync**. Due to a fault in the recorder or sound transfer, the sound and picture progressively drift apart.

slo-mo (USA) Slow motion or freeze-frame facility on a videotape machine.

slow motion Apparent slowing down of action achieved by running the film faster than normal speed in the camera and then projecting at the normal rate.

slug 1. Piece of blank film leader used as a spacer or to replace a damaged section on a work print. **2.** In News/Current Affairs, the working title of a story.

slung Lighting suspended from an overhead grid. Scenery is always described as being flown.

slung mike Fixed microphone suspended from the set or lighting grid.

small giraffe See **lazy arm**.

smear Distortion of a video image when there is a sharp contrast between subject and background and the outline appears to smudge. Could be caused by a fault, a worn-out camera tube or low-light levels.

smoke candle Type of firework used to generate smoke on location.

smoke gun Apparatus which generates smoke for special effects.

snake arm L-shaped accessory used on jibs to give extra high or low-angle shots.

sneak in/out Surreptitiously to put in something missing or remove an embarrassment on a set without the audience noticing. Done whilst the camera is off-air.

snipe Low-level camera mounting.

snoop tracks Continuous recording of dialogue in the studio or on location as a safety measure for post-production.

snoot Narrow-ended metal cone fitted to a lamp to give a narrow circle of light.

snorkel Periscope attachment for a camera lens.

snow Effect caused by electrical noise resulting in an apparent blizzard of white speckles on a television screen.

snow job Newsroom reference to a whitewash. An attempt to produce a flattering picture of a person or subject by suppressing inconvenient information.

snow loop Continuous loop of film either projected and printed or played through a telecine machine and superimposed over a scene to suggest a blizzard.

snow machine Machine which can blow torn pieces of paper or other material to simulate snowfall.

snow remover Electronic digital equipment to remove noise in a video picture.

snuff movie Sado-pornographic film in which performers are lingeringly done to death. The ultimate in sexploitation schlock.

soap opera/soaps A long-running drama series, set in a specific community with a large cast and a number of plot lines running simultaneously. The greatest audience puller on television. Originally developed in the USA for housebound wives and sponsored by soap and detergent manufacturers.

Society of Motion Picture & Television Engineers (SMPTE) Professional body with branches in the USA and the UK which defines professional standards for technical apparatus.

Sod's Law See **Murphy's Law**.

soft A shot slightly out-of-focus, by design or accident.

soft core movies Pornographic movies pretending to be other genres and tailored to avoid censorship or prosecution.

soft edge Facility in a studio console for blurring the boundary between two pictures, e.g. in a wipe or chromakey effect.

soft focus Blurred effect from a lens not correctly focused achieved by design, frequently by accident. A technique sometimes affected by commercial film makers to suggest dreamy romanticism.

soft light A lamp without a tightly focused, hard-edged beam, used normally as a filler.

soft sell Commercial technique which promotes a brand by use of humour or by assuming sentimental, if irrelevant, associations between the product and objects of delight, i.e. suggesting an affinity between cuddly labrador puppies and lavatory paper. See **hard sell**.

soft story An interesting story without an important topical content which is none the less considered worthy of inclusion in a magazine or news bulletin.

solarisation Electronic visual effect involving tone reversals of highlights and shadows.

solid state **1.** Modern technical equipment not using valves. **2.** Generic term applied to transistor electronic equipment when compared with thermonic (valve) electron units.

son-in-law Archaic Hollywood term of contempt for the director, often reputed to have got the job by marrying the producer's daughter.

song sheet Television gallery slang for a script or running order.

Sony U-matic videotape (SUM) Manufacturer's name for a particular format of videotape recorders.

sound Audible vibrations.

sound advance Editing technique of leading the sound track or dialogue of an incoming scene over the outgoing one, prior to the picture cut.

sound balance The process of balancing the sound from two or more sources.

sound bay Area in a dubbing theatre where the sound tracks are replayed, each machine being referred to as a bay, even when in the same location.

sound bite A brief interview or overlaid comment in a news or informational programme.

sound booth The box in which a commentator or performer sits to read words to pictures in a dubbing theatre.

sound camera A camera designed to record sound on a magnetic strip or to stay in synchronism with an audio tape recorder.

sound cart/cartridge 1/4-inch sound cassette used on radio for signature tunes, jingles, etc.

sound control 1. The process of connecting up, balancing, recording and transmitting sound. 2. The room in a studio where this is done.

sound drum Roller used to smooth out movement of film across a sound head in a projector.

sound editor A film editor on a large production who is solely responsible for the collection and laying of sound tracks for a subsequent dub.

sound effects (FX) Recorded or manufactured sounds used mainly at the dubbing process of film or VT to add dramatic impact to a sound track.

sound filters/audio filters Devices used to modify sound quality, usually by reducing either higher or lower frequencies on a recorded sound track.

sound head 1. Device to detect and transfer sound signals on to tape or film. 2. Transport mechanism for the sound track in a film projector.

sound in syncs (SIS) Method of distributing sound by digitally encoding it into the sync period of the picture, thus avoiding the need for additional high-quality sound lines.

sound loop A length of magnetic sound tape joined at the ends, which may be played indefinitely to give a continuous background sound.

sound man A sound recordist, gramophone or boom operator or any other member of an operational sound crew. But, more particularly, refers to the supervisor in charge of the sound crew.

sound on film (SOF) 1. Film with its own magnetic or optical sound track printed alongside the picture. 2. Sometimes used in news scripts to indicate any film with sound, as distinct from mute film requiring commentary or effects to be added on transmission.

sound on tape (SOT/SOVT) Videotape in which the original recorded sound is to be used.

sound on vision (SOV) 1. (USA) Fault in which a sound signal causes interference or break up of a television picture. 2. (USA) Voice-over script.

sound perspective Effect of controlling volume and the distance of subjects from a microphone to give an impression of distance.

sound positive Photographic print of an optical sound track. See **commopt**.

sound proofing Acoustic treatment of scenery or studio walls to eliminate disturbing outside noise and improve the acoustics within.

sound reader A small loudspeaker connected to the sound tracks of a synchroniser.

sound recording Audio recording.

sound reverberation Reflected sound occurring naturally or electronically as an effect.

sound sheet The log sheet prepared by the recordist at the end of a day's shoot, for use by the sound transfer suite and the film or video editor.

sound shooting The recording of action sound as well as pictures.

sound speed The accepted speed at which film passes through a camera or projector. Cinema speed is normally 24 frames per second; in the majority of television systems this is modified to 25 frames per second.

sound stage A sound-proofed studio suitable for recording live sound.

sound supervisor The person responsible for the sound quality of a programme in a studio or OB and also responsible for the sound crew.

sound sweetening (USA) See **sweetening.**

sound test Audition of an actor's voice.

sound track 1. An individually recorded tape or disc in post-production. 2. The physical area of a commag or commopt film carrying the sound information.

sound transfer Technical area in which original 1/4-inch sound tapes or effects discs are transferred on to 16mm sprocketed magnetic film track for synchronisation and track laying in the cutting room.

soup Slang term for film processing or, in particular, the chemical solution in which it is done.

source music (USA) See **foreground music.**

Southern TV Commercial company once controlling the English southern IBA franchise area. Subsequently replaced by TVS (Television South).

spacer Blank film used to fill gaps between sound tracks in the track-laying process.

sparkle White speckling on a film print caused by dust on the original negative or by wear or interference on a videotape.

sparks A lighting electrician.

speaker See **loudspeaker**.

speaking extra A performer who may be required to speak as part of the crowd, without having definite lines incorporated in the script.

spear carrier A walk-on performer.

special effects Either manufactured events on location such as explosions, smoke, rain, etc, or in post-production with video or film laboratory techniques rather than in reality. Also called visual effects. See **mattes**, **CSO**.

special effects generator A device for creating electronic effects such as wipes, CSO, etc. See also **digital video effects**.

specifications/specs Technical standards laid down by broadcast engineers hence '*up to spec*' or '*not up to spec*'. Specs are variable. See **modify**, **tweak**.

spectrum A range of wavelengths or frequencies of acoustic or electromagnetic radiation, in particular, a display of visible light arranged in order of wavelength.

specular A very bright, non-diffused reflection from a polished surface, e.g. jewellery completely overloading the camera if it inadvertently reflects light into the camera, or a sparkling highlight deliberately created with a star filter.

speech track A voice or dialogue track as

opposed to music or effects in track laying.

speed 1. Linear movement of a film or tape. 2. Lens light-gathering potential. 3. Sensitivity of a film emulsion. 4. Verbal confirmation given by sound recordist that the machine is running, after hearing the director's instruction *'turn over!'*.

spherical aberration A defect in poor-quality lenses where peripheral rays of light meet at a different focal point from axial rays.

spider Moveable spreader on rollers mounted under a tripod to enable it to dolly on very smooth surfaces.

spider box A portable junction box for the multi-plugging of lamps or mikes.

spike To discard a newsroom story or a piece of copy. Derived from Fleet Street where unwanted sheets of copy were impaled on a metal spike.

spill Unwanted light from an incorrectly adjusted lamp.

spill ring An attachment fitted to a spotlight that stops light emanating from the sides of a spotlight instead of passing through the lens.

spin off Exploitation of a successful programme by sales of souvenirs, records, books, etc, or by making another programme using some characters in a different setting, e.g. *Knots Landing* using characters from *Dallas*.

splatter/splat movie Genre of low film involving the systematic extermination of most of the cast in the most gruesome circumstances the producer can afford. See **schlock**.

splice To join two lengths of film together by transparent tape or film cement.

splicing tape Transparent adhesive tape used for making film joins in the cutting room or for joining sound tape.

split edit An edit in film or videotape in which the sound and picture cuts are not simultaneous.

split focus Cameraman's technique for trying to film simultaneously two subjects in deep focus by focusing on a point equidistant between the two, giving an acceptable image of both, but optimum sharpness on neither.

split reel A film reel on which the two sides come apart, allowing a projectionist to remove a film without having to rewind.

split screen Division across the screen between two scenes, so that two halves of an action can be seen simultaneously, e.g. both ends of a telephone conversation.

split track Sound recording on location with a portable video camera in which the recordist simultaneously uses the two available audio tracks on the videotape for final mixing later.

splitter A cable junction box with one input and a number of outputs.

spoiler 1. Where a television company hastily launches a similar type of programme or one on the same subject in advance of a rival company's production. 2. Pins used to prevent head-to-tape contact during fast wind or rewind. 3. Impractical electronic system to prevent members of the public from copying records or CD's to compact cassette.

sponsorship Means of financing programmes by direct funding from an outside agency which usually has editorial control of the end product.

spool The flanged reel on which videotape or sound tape is wound.

spool box Film magazine on a projector.

spoonerism Verbal fluff where syllables become transposed in successive words, e.g. Gorse Hards Parade, *The Will in the*

Windows, The Bum of the Flightlebee. Cause of much mirth at the expense of newsreaders.

spot 1. To cue a VT recording at the chosen point. 2. To focus a hard light source. 3. A general name for a focused handlight. 4. General reference to a specific sequence in a programme, e.g. interview spot. 5. Small VT reel used for advertisements, etc.

spot check The check carried out at the end of a recording to make sure that the programme has indeed been recorded on to tape.

spot effects Sound effects which are done on the set or at a dub, e.g. a knock at a door, footsteps, which are not pre-recorded.

spotlight A hard light source.

Spotlight An annual compendium of British actors and actresses.

spotting Locating individual sounds in a sound recording.

spread 1. Floor manager's instruction to performers to pad out their acts to fill time. **2.** (USA) See **overrun**.

spreader A folding framework into which the spiked legs of a film tripod can be fitted to avoid making holes in people's carpets.

sprocket A wheel with accurately spaced teeth to engage the sprocket holes along a piece of film.

sprocket holes Perforations in film.

sprung platform Stage mounted on springs, manually operated to give the effect in close shots of the interior of a rowing boat, moving vehicle, etc.

spun Translucent, gauze-like material made of fibre glass which can be pegged over the barn doors of a lamp to diffuse the light.

spurious signal Unwanted noise signal in audio or video.

sputnik A 2kw studio lamp so-called because of its round shape, reminiscent of early space satellites.

squawk box Small loudspeaker or intercom.

squeeze Electronic digital video effect in which the picture is distorted by being compressed vertically or horizontally towards its centre.

squeeze zoom Trade name for a device that manipulates the geometry of a picture, now used generically. See **squeeze**.

squelch Circuit in an FM radio receiver which mutes the output when the strength of incoming signal drops below a set level to minimise background noise.

squib Electrical firing device used to make detonations of small explosive charges on a set or costume simulating bullet hits.

stage 1. To mount a drama production.
2. A raised platform on which artists perform.
3. A film studio.

stage brace An adjustable prop to hold up flats and other scenery generally held in place by a stage weight at ground level.

stage cloth Canvas cloth floor covering, often painted to simulate stone flagging, woodblocks, etc.

stage direction 1. The planning and execution of a theatrical production in terms of performance of the artists, timing, the cueing of effects, etc. **2.** Instruction for performer's movements designated in the script or delivered by the director.

stage-hand/studio-hand A person who assists in the theatre/studio with the setting of scenery and props, operating hoists, etc.

stage left/right Left and right as perceived by a performer facing an auditorium or a camera. Opposite of **camera left/right**.

stage manager 1. (non-BBC TV) The equivalent of the BBC AFM (assistant floor manager) responsible for props and artists' calls. **2.** (OB) The equivalent of the floor manager in the studio.

stage weight An iron weight used to support scenery and hold stage braces.

stagger through Early rehearsal in which the artists go through a continuous performance, but with stops to solve technical problems.

staging plan (USA) See **floorplan**.

staircase (USA) See **step wedge test signal**.

stairstep /step Test signal. See **step wedge**.

stake out Journalese for hanging around unobtrusively near a location waiting for anticipated action to occur or a subject to appear.

stake out a pitch To lay claim to a favourable situation for a reporter or for a camera position.

stand 1. Platform for a musical conductor.
2. Support for a microphone, sheet music or a studio caption. **3.** Old name for a one-off performance or gig.

stand by! Call by director or production manager for a unit and cast to be prepared for the beginning of a take. When everyone is at their mark the order is given *'turn over!'* in film, or *'cue!'* or *'go!'* (if it is a sound cue) in studios.

stand by one/two/three! (USA) Gallery instruction to a cameraman that he will be taking a shot shortly and should be steady and in focus.

stand down To dismiss a crew at a break in a rehearsal or recording for a period of time.

stand-in An actor used normally in a long shot to substitute for a main performer in a scene, e.g. in action sequences or during lengthy camera rehearsals.

stand-up comic Comedian who tells jokes directly to the microphone or an audience.

stand-upper Part of a topical programme in which a reporter, frequently clutching a hand microphone, addresses the camera. See **piece to camera, reporter**.

standby 1. Equipment or staff reserved in case events go on beyond the length of time originally planned or in case an emergency call-out is required because of sickness or a sudden programme requirement. **2.** A condition of reduced power that leaves equipment in a state of readiness for immediate deployment without having the equipment fully operational. **3.** An item that can be slotted into a programme should another item overrun or have to be dropped.

standby crew Team of craftsmen on standby in

studio centres or on major locations responsible for last-minute pointing, repairs to the set, construction work, etc.

Standard 8 Original format of 8mm film.

standards conversion The translation of one TV scanning standard to another, e.g. from American 525 lines to the European 625 lines, before it can be transmitted.

star Someone who has actually played a leading role on film or TV and so is one up on a celebrity. Much sought after by personalities or compères, who rate lower than either.

star filter Camera filter of clear glass etched with a reflective grid pattern which causes highlights to be radiated as a star pattern.

star trail Digital video effect in which an image is made to trail random pixels giving an effect similar to the film cartoon animation of magic stardust .

starburst lens Special lens which dramatises highlights by creating star-shaped flares of light.

starlet Obsolete term for a young actress, contracted by a company more for her looks than her talent.

start mark Mark upon the beginning of a piece of film to help synchronisation of sound and picture before projection.

state-of-the-art Pomposity to describe this year's model, supposedly technical equipment of the very latest design and capabilities.

static 1. Interference on sound or vision.
2. Static electricity which can build up from friction in technical areas and which can give rise to unexpected electrical shocks.

station break (USA) Legally obligatory break, normally at fifteen-minute intervals, in which a station must identify itself, its call sign and channel number.

station ident See **station break**.

Steadicam Gyroscopically-controlled or counter-weighted camera harness designed to enable relatively steady hand-held shots.

Steenbeck A make of film editing tables and equipment.

steering wheel (USA) A tiller on an electronic camera pedestal.

stencilling Creating patterns by painting over cut outs or using a patterned roller to create effects such as wallpaper on a stage set.

step printer Film printing machine which operates frame-by-frame, used for slowing-down or speeding-up motion or for preparing freeze frame.

step wedge/step 1. A test waveform that has a number of levels (steps) of brightness from black on the left side of screen to white on the right. 2. Series of controlled exposures on a sample batch of photographic materials.

stereo/stereophony Sound recording in which the sound is recorded on two channels from microphones in a particular geographic relationship and replayed in a manner that preserves that geographical relationship to give an impression of space and depth to a recording.

stereoscopic Pictures produced from two slightly displaced viewpoints which combine to give a three-dimensional effect.

stick mike A robust, hand-held microphone much beloved by reporters.

sticks Synonym for **tripod**.

still frame Continuous reproduction of one frame of picture, either film or video. Also called **freeze frame**.

stills Transparencies, film prints and graphic artwork used in a studio.

stills store Library of still frames stored electronically, replacing the traditional stills on photographic slide transparencies. See **slide file**.

sting A short musical phrase, sometimes accompanying pictures, used to punctuate transitions from one scene or one item to another.

stippling Scene painting effect in which a coarse brush is used to dabble paint of a darker or lighter tone on to the background colour to suggest stonework.

stock Film footage. Whilst still unexposed referred to as raw stock.

stock sets Flattage and furniture of various periods and styles kept for repeated use in different programmes with minimal refurbishment.

stock shots/footage General, non-specific shots, often saved from the trims of programmes which can be used again in later productions, e.g. views of buildings, aeroplanes taking off and landing, etc. See **library footage**.

stop Lens aperture size, normally quoted in f numbers, e.g. from $f/5.6$ to $f/4.0$ or $f/2.8$ to $f/2.0$. One stop is equivalent to doubling the light-gathering power.

stop down To reduce the aperture of the lens.

stop frame 1. System of optically printing film at the laboratories to achieve freeze frames and special effects. 2. Method of shooting film frame-by-frame for rostrum camera work and animation. See **update**.

stop marks Scale of numbers around a film lens indicating the size of aperture and expressed as f numbers, e.g. 2.8, 4.0, 5.6.

stop motion 1. A freeze frame. 2. Animation

techniques in which a camera operates at single frames or two frames at a time whilst the subject is moved between exposures, or artwork is manipulated.

stop over/under Exposure which is over or under-exposed by a number of *f* stops.

stop printing See **double framing**.

stop pull The technique of changing the stop on a lens during a shot to cope with changing contrast, e.g. whilst panning from a light area to a shaded one during the action. Usually done by the assistant cameraman or focus puller.

stopping Fixing a film after development by immersing it in a second bath of chemicals to neutralise the developing solution on the emulsion and fix the image.

story editor Old BBC name for **script editor**.

storyboard Pictorial cartoon representation of a director's intention depicting a narrative, scene-by-scene or shot-by-shot. Always used before shooting begins in animated sequences, the production of film commercials, or complex CSO/chromakey sequences.

straight man One of a team of two comedians who deliberately acts as a foil to the funny man. In Hollywood sometimes called the number two banana.

strand A number of programmes at regular time slots dealing with a defined subject matter.

Strand Electric Part of the Rank group of companies which manufacture and distribute stage and studio lighting equipment.

strap easel Caption stand with weighted straps to hold large captions, open books, etc, in place.

straplines Name captions or subtitles which are superimposed on a strap of colour overlaid on the image.

straws Amber-coloured filters for lamps.

streaking Distortion of the low-frequency components of a television picture.

stretch A signal from a floor manager to a presenter indicating a sequence is under-running and the presenter needs to fill in time. See **spread**.

stretch filming Film techniques for extending a sequence by printing individual frames more than once. A long stretch results in the appearance of a freeze frame.

stretch print/stretch printing See **stretch filming**.

strike To take down a set after completing production or to remove a prop from a scene.

stringer A journalist or cameraman, either freelance or employed by someone else, who can be called upon to follow up a story in the absence of a regular, locally-based correspondent or crew.

strip chart Breakdown of shooting days, deployment of crews and artists, etc, used as the basis for planning an extensive drama shoot.

stripe Term for commag film in which the sound track is carried by a thin strip of magnetic tape printed alongside the film picture print.

striping The process of applying a magnetic sound track to an edited film, used by amateur film makers.

stripping Technique of scheduling television programmes (particularly mini-series) on successive nights with the intention of maximising audience.

strobe Lighting effect caused by deliberately flickering a lamp. Also used to describe the unwanted similar effect caused by panning a camera too fast, rotating objects interfering with the picture field rate, etc.

stroboscope A rapidly flashing discharge lamp.

stroboscopic effect/strobing The jerky motion effect caused by a flashing light on movement.

studio The enclosed working area for television, radio or stills photography production. In feature films, the studio is often used as a collective term for a site containing several individual film stages.

studio apparatus room The area associated with a studio that houses the non-operational technical equipment.

studio flat An element of scenery used to construct sets.

studio manager 1. Principal technician in a radio studio. 2. (USA) A television floor manager.

studio ops/operations Department of scenic workers in a studio.

studio plan A floor plan of a studio, showing the arrangement of sets.

stuntman/stuntwoman A specialist who stands in for an artist to perform energetic and potentially dangerous actions.

style book Book laying down rules for the use of language, grammar and layout, defining the house-style of a newspaper or programme.

stylus Sapphire or diamond needle used to record or replay gramophone records.

styrofoam (USA) Polystyrene.

sub editor/sub Newsroom journalist who writes or edits copy submitted by reporters, news agencies, etc.

sub-control room/sub CR A control room, without an associated studio, used for post-production purposes or for pre-mixing major programmes with a large number of sources (e.g. general elections) or as a substitute control room at times of refurbishment or catastrophic failure.

subcarrier Signal used to interleave the colour in a normal TV picture signal.

subjective camera Style of direction in which the camera is used almost as a character to involve the audience in a scene, as opposed to objective camerawork which holds back and observes the action as from an auditorium.

subjective eyeline (USA) See **point-of-view** shot.

subjective track Also known as tracking POV (point of view) shot. The cameraman simulates the viewpoint of an artist by panning or tracking in his/her place.

subscription television System for paying for television programmes by subscriptions gathered from the viewers. The main source of revenue for public service broadcasting in the USA.

substandard Obsolete term to describe film gauges smaller than 35mm, e.g. 8mm, etc.

subtitle Superimposed, printed translation of foreign or indistinct speech.

subtitler The machine or person who puts subtitles on film or video programmes.

subtractive process Colour process of film emulsions using magenta, cyan and yellow. The additive process uses the broadcasting primaries red, blue and green.

sugar glass Easily shattered substitute for glasses, bottles, etc, used where real glass would constitute a danger. Originally molten sugar though, latterly, types of resin are used.

sun arc Alternative term for **carbon arc**.

sun gun A hand-held battery light.

supalock An obsolete method of rapidly synchronising an overlay.

super 1. See **superimpose. 2.** (theatre) An extra.

super cards See **name cards/super**.

Super 8 Modern format for 8mm film, the picture and sprocket holes being of a different geometry to standard eight giving a larger picture area.

super high frequency (SHF) 3GHz - 30GHz.

Super 16 System of shooting 16mm film without the use of anamorphic lenses for projection on wide cinema screens. Film geometry is different from 16mm and the film passes the gate horizontally instead of vertically.

superimpose (S/I) The combination of two images so that both remain distinctly in vision, e.g. name captions over the image of a speaker.

supervising editor The editor-in-charge in a feature film, in which two or more cutting rooms are operating simultaneously.

supplementary lens Additional lens fitted over a prime lens, normally for extra close shooting. See **diopter**.

supporting artist A major theatrical role, but not one of the main leading characters, cast to be played by stars.

supporting artiste An **extra**.

suppression The reduction of RF interference.

surface noise Unwanted noise such as hiss and crackle on a record or from the soundtrack of a film.

surround-sound An arrangement of loudspeakers that surrounds the listener with sound, usually from quadrophonic recordings.

swag A drape arranged in hanging folds creating a curtain effect.

swan Derisive term for an expenses-paid trip with no obvious benefit to a production.

sweep A curved rail from which a cyclorama or drapes can be suspended.

sweetening Process of balancing and redubbing sound tracks on an edited on-line videotape.

swing a lens Obsolete term for changing the lens on a turret camera by rotating the disc on which the different angle lenses are mounted.

swinger A hinged flat at the end of a set which can be quickly swung into place to prevent cameras shooting off.

swish pan (USA) See **whip pan**.

switched talkback Talkback circuit between the studio gallery and a presenter, controlled by a switch and normally received through a deaf aid.

switched viewfinders Technical facility of studio cameras enabling one cameraman to view the output of another through his viewfinder in order to match his shot.

switcher (USA) See **vision mixer**.

switchgear The mains breakers, switches, fuses, etc, to power up a major facility, e.g. a studio, OB, or lighting rig.

sync See **synchronism**.

sync bench The work bench in a film cutting room.

sync lead Cable between a film camera and its recorder carrying the signals which synchronise one with the other.

sync level Amplitude of sync pulses of a TV picture signal.

sync mark A cross on a film leader or the lines marked with a wax pencil on the magnetic tape used by film editors to get sound and picture in synchronism.

sync motor A motor whose rotation speed is controlled by the frequency of a reference signal or of AC mains.

sync sound Synchronous sound, recorded on location.

synchroniser **1.** Film cutting room equipment upon which film pictures and a number of sound tracks can be laid in parallel on linked sprocket wheels. See **pic sync**, **compeditor**. **2.** Digital frame store allowing video source to be synchronised with local sources.

synchronising pulse **1.** One of the pulses generated by the SPG which appears in its own right on vision signals and which is used to synchronise subsequent equipment and drive TV scanning waveforms. **2.** Signal from a film camera recorded on a track of an audio tape recorder for preserving synchronisation during sound transfer.

synchronising pulse generator (SPG) The heart of the studio. The device that generates all the electronic pulses which create the television waveform and synchronise all the equipment.

synchronism **1.** Exact matching of pictures and sound. **2.** Exact timing of picture sources that enables cutting, mixing, etc, without disturbance to the output, i.e. the pulses from both sources are exactly timed together. Abbreviated to **sync**.

synchronous orbit A satellite orbit where the rotation is the same as that of the earth. See **geostationary satellite**.

synthesizer **1.** Part of a studio gallery equipment which can change the colouring of captions. **2.** An electronic sound generator for producing sound effects or electronic music. **3.** A device for generating related frequencies from a single base frequency.

Sypher BBC term for **Synchronous Post dub Helical-scan** VT. A system for dubbing post-production sound on videotape using multi-track sound magnetic tapes.

system design The detailed overall plan of a technical facility.

TAM See **Television Audience Measurement**.

T & D See **travel & duty**.

TARIF See **Technical Apparatus for the Rectification of Indifferent Film**.

TASS USSR news agency.

TBA Script abbreviation for **to be arranged**, i.e. not confirmed at the time of typing.

TBC See **time base corrector**.

TC See **technical co-ordinator** or **telecine**.

tel op Abbreviation for **television scenic operative**.

TJ See **telejector**.

TK See **telecine**.

TM See **technical manager**.

TOIL See **time off in lieu**.

TR See **telerecording**.

TSW See **Television South West**.

TV International abbreviation for **television**.

TVE See **Television Trust for the Environment**.

TVS See **Television South**.

TW3 See *That Was The Week That Was*.

TX See **transmission**. Also abbreviation for **transmitter**.

T-number/T-stop A method of calibration of a lens based on the actual light transmission through the optics at various apertures.

tab track A theatre curtain rail.

tabs 1. Stage curtains. **2.** Markers attached to a film to cue or identify a section of film. See **paper up**.

tachometer A transducer that converts rotation speed into a scale indication, e.g. in variable speed cameras or projectors graduated in frames per second.

tag The last line of a broadcast commercial

intended to leave a lasting impression in the mind.

tag line A script line that has to be hit at a certain fixed point in a programme to cue a transition or new item.

tail out A film which has not been rewound and which therefore, if projected, would begin at the end. Also called **end out**.

take A single camera shot. See **slate**, **board**.

take a beat Make a brief dramatic pause before cueing a continuation of a speech or action.

take bar Facility on certain vision mixing consoles whereby cuts can be programmed in advance, leaving the operator simply to hit a single button.

take one!/two!/three! **1.** Film term for a shot as marked on a clapperboard and recorded on the shot list. **2.** (USA) Studio direction term for **cut to**.

take super! (USA) Instruction to a vision mixer from a director to superimpose pictures on to another, usually a graphic name caption or the like.

take-up spool The spool on a camera, projector, tape recorder or editing table, which winds the film or tape from the feed spool after it has passed through the gate or passed the heads.

talent Word leading to misunderstanding between speakers of British and American English. British: a God-given ability or gift, e.g. he has a talent for dancing. American: a performer, actor or anyone who gets in front of a camera lens. Has a curious plural form, i.e. an actor is 'a talent' whereas two or more are 'the talent'.

talkback The sound link between the studio gallery and the technical and production staff in the studio.

talking head An interviewee or presenter, in any kind of close-up shot, talking.

tally light (USA) Cue light which indicates which camera is on in a multi-camera studio.

Tanjug Yugoslav news agency.

tank Reservoir in a processing machine that contains a chemical solution.

tape Non-perforated magnetic strip used for recording sound or pictures. Perforated strips are called magnetic film. See **commag**.

tape deck Working top of a sound tape recorder.

tape editing The physical cutting and joining of magnetic tape or the electronic manipulation of videotape programmes.

tape library A library for recorded sound or videotapes.

tape recorder A machine for recording sound and/or pictures on to plastic coated tape with a magnetically sensitive layer. See **rust**.

tape splice A join between two sections of tape made with adhesive tape.

tape transport Mechanism for moving audio or videotape past the heads in a tape recorder.

tape up To simulate the position of flats, doors, etc, in a rehearsal room by marking the floor with coloured adhesive tapes. To mark up.

target 1. Screen within a TV tube on to which electron beams from the cathode are projected. 2. Alternative name for **French flag**.

target audience The segment of the viewing audience at which a particular programme or commercial is aimed.

tarpaulin Canvas or plastic sheet used to cover and protect equipment or, painted, to simulate a surface in open-air locations.

tat See **schlock**.

tearing Characteristic of video cameras when the contrast ratio of a scene is too great; the line between light and dark parts of the scene appear to fray and tear apart. Also, a similar fault on videotape recorders more usually known as **bearding**.

tease/teaser Headline or hook at the head of a programme to persuade the viewer to remain with the programme. A very brief sequence in a junction between programmes advertising a forth-coming transmission.

Technical Apparatus for the Rectification of Indifferent Film (TARIF) A means whereby a telecine operator can modify the density of colour balance of a projected film according to his taste. This is not always the same taste as that of the director, film editor and laboratory colour grader who made the show print in the first place.

technical co-ordinator (TC) One of the titles in use for the senior engineer or technician in charge of a studio, the technical director.

technical manager(TM) An out-dated term for the senior technician in charge of a studio.

technical producer (USA) The senior technician on a production. A term used extensively around the world, but little used in the UK.

technical run/tech run Run through of a complete production at outside rehearsal, specifically for the lighting and sound engineers.

Technicolor Early colour film process.

tele-conferencing Commercial use of TV studios and outside broadcast equipment in which various centres are linked together for conferences and discussions without being transmitted on a public network.

telecast (USA) Television.

telecasting (USA) Television broadcasting.

telecine System for converting film into electronic signals for television transmission.

Normally abbreviated **TC**, but by the BBC, **TK** to avoid confusion with Television Centre.

telecine chain A complete telecine installation.

telecine run-on Technique of joining a number of film sequences together with blank tape or leaders between to a fixed length, so that a presenter comes back into vision between extracts and the telecine machine runs continuously.

Telecom Abbreviation for British Telecom, the national telecommunications company.

telecommunication The linking of two locations by radio signals.

telecourse (USA) Education programme linked to a course of study. See **Open University, Open College.**

telediphone Obsolete system of recording live programmes off-air on to discs, from which accurate transcripts can be made.

telejector (TJ) Slide projector coupled to a video camera for transmitting stills.

telephoto Term for any narrow-angle long lens, particularly in stills photography. Strictly an arrangement of lenses to produce a combination with a longer focal length than its physical length.

teleprinter A printer and keyboard for receiving and sending messages over a communications network. See **rip and read.**

teleprompt System of running an enlarged written script in front of a studio television camera as a prompt for a newsreader or presenter.

telerecording **1.** Obsolete way of recording on to film a programme originating from an electronic studio. Many old programmes survive only in their telerecorded mode. **2.** Now the process of transferring videotape to film, e.g. for editing purposes.

telescope An extending lighting or microphone support.

telestrator An early technique for drawing images directly on to the TV screen.

Teletel French viewdata service.

teletext General term for a data service transmitted in the blanking interval of the TV waveform.

telethon A type of live television programme, usually used to raise money for charity, in which an entire evening of transmission is built around publicity for a particular cause.

televiewers (USA) The television audience.

television The transmission of pictures by radio signals.

Television Audience Measurement (TAM) Audience research bureau sponsored by the UK commercial TV companies and later absorbed into the British Audience Research Bureau.

television camera A device for converting pictures into electronic signals.

television grey scale **1.** The range of contrast from black to white. **2.** A test card or signal used to line up cameras.

Television South (TVS) Commercial television company broadcasting to the Southern and south eastern counties of England.

Television South West (TSW) Commercial company covering the south-west of England.

Television Trust for the Environment (TVE). Non profit-making company launched by Central TV with United Nations backing to encourage programmes about natural sciences and the environment.

television white The white that can be handled by the contrast range of a television camera. In fact a shade of very light grey.

telex An international communication system over the public telegraphy network, using keyboards and teleprinter terminals.

Telidon Canadian viewdata service.

tenlight Soft light comprising a bank of ten incandescent lamps switched individually or in groups.

terminal Fixed cable connections or work stations at the end of a communications network.

test card A pattern on a card or slide which technicians use to adjust cameras, monitors and receivers for their optimum performance.

test equipment Apparatus for the measurement of equipment performance and fault finding, e.g. oscilloscope, multi-meter, etc.

test pattern See **test card**.

test signal A signal generated to test the performance of the transmission chain. See **tone**.

test signal generator A device for generating signals which can be used to test the performance of equipment and circuits.

test tape A pre-recorded tape for lining up tape recorders.

Tewe lens Portable zoom lens on a lanyard used as a viewfinder to frame shots, worn about the neck by directors as a mark of status.

text Written part of a programme. The script.

Thames Television London commercial company with the television franchise serving the Greater London region on weekdays only.

That Was The Week That Was (TW3) Pioneering satirical current affairs review of the 1960's. See **Lord Privy Seal**.

Theatre TV Programme played on a projection screen for an invited or paying audience, usually to record their applause and reactions for transmission.

theme 1. A musical signature for a programme.
2. The argument in a documentary programme.
3. A tune or motif which is repeated to identify places or persons.

thespian An actor or actress.

thin Description of an image lacking in density on film, usually due to over-exposure, or a recorded sound lacking in low frequencies.

thirty-five millimetre (35mm) Commonest feature film gauge before being displaced by wide screen formats. Remains the commonest still photography format, but on television restricted for cost reasons to graphics work and very prestigous productions. See **academy frame**.

threading Lacing up a film or tape in a machine.

three-colour process Normal film and television additive colour system, in which the visible spectrum is split into the three primary components, red, blue and green.

three-machine editing Videotape facility using two replay machines and one recording machine, allowing the operator to perform mixes and other effects.

three-phase The distribution of mains power along four wires, three live and one neutral. The voltages along each live (or 'phase') wire are separated in time by one third of a cycle (i.e. 120 degrees) of mains frequency, resulting in domestic/industrial distribution in the UK of 415 volts between phases and 240 volts between any phase and neutral.

three-point lighting The basic lighting technique for portraiture, using keylight, backlight and filler.

threshold 1. The lowest level at which a sound

or picture can be perceived. **2.** The minimum exposure to produce a detectable density after processing. **3.** The point at which an audience loses interest in a programme and wants to change channels. See **zap**.

through the lens (TTL) Viewfinder system of a camera that looks directly through the lens. See **single lens reflex**.

throw 1. The direct distance between the projector and the screen, sometimes reduced in studio projection by the use of mirrors. **2.** The distance between a lamp and a subject.

throw focus To pull focus in a shot from the foreground to the background or vice versa.

thumbsucker Seemingly profound, scripted pay-off line in a current affairs programme, e.g.*'one thing is certain, things will never be the same again!'*.

thunder sheet A large sheet of thin metal which can be flexed to produce the sound of thunder.

thyristor A semi-conductor device often used as a power controller, e.g. in lighting dimmers.

tie line A physical cable link between two areas.

tie-in (USA) Commercial plug given by an announcer at the end of a bulletin or magazine programme acknowledging the sponsor of the programme or an advertiser.

Tiffen A make of camera filters.

tight 1. Description of a live show with a very critical timing. **2.** The condition in which the director of same is likely to be found afterwards.

tight shot Close-up shot in which the subject fills the screen, more commonly used of objects than of performers when the terms close-up, mid close-up, etc, are used.

tiller bar/wheel The steering wheel on an electronic pedestal camera.

tilt Moving a lens vertically on its axis up or down.

time base corrector (TBC) A device that accepts unstable signals (e.g. from a VTR) or from a non-synchronised source, and produces an output that is stable and synchronised to local sources.

time code An electronic signal which gives a unique number to each frame on a recorded videotape. Usually related to time in hours, minutes, seconds and frames. This can then be

TIGHT

displayed as a window or separately upon replay to aid the editor in the same way as rubber numbers on film. It can also be used to instruct sophisticated edit controllers and hold VTR's in precise synchronisation.

time cue A cue taken from a master clock in stations where scheduling is run as an automated operation.

time division multiplex Method for simultaneously transmitting more than one digitally encoded signal along the same path.

time lapse Photography which condenses time by locking the camera in a fixed position and shooting frame-by-frame over a long period, e.g. to show a flower opening or a cloud moving over a sky.

time off in lieu (TOIL) Term used to describe compensatory time off given to technicans in place of, or additional to, overtime or penalty payments. See **days off in lieu**.

time out (USA) A break in a rehearsal in which the cast or crew are stood down.

time slot The place of a programme in a broadcast schedule.

time-gamma-temperature curve A graphic display of the relationship between the development time of film, the gamma or contrast reproduction, and the temperature of the developing solution.

time-shift viewing Result of the spread of domestic video recorders where people record programmes off-air and then watch at other times.

timing The pacing of a performance by an actor to give dramatic meaning to a scene, or through shots cut together by a film or VT editor.

tin pan alley Obsolete term for the popular

music industry. Specifically Denmark Street in London's Soho, once the centre for this activity.

tin snips Wire cutters.

tip projection Penetration depth of a video head into videotape, the amount of protrusion beyond the head drum.

tip-off fee Fee paid to a freelance journalist or public informant for a lead to a news story.

Titan A large camera crane.

title Written name of a programme or performer superimposed over a scene.

title key See **downstream keyer**.

to camera Speaking directly to the camera lens in the style of a newsreader or reporter.

Toblerone A block of wood, triangular in cross-section, used to carry a name on a desk, or a more sophisticated device, in which several vertically-linked triangular bars can be rotated on their axis to present different surfaces to the camera. Often used with chromakey. Named after a Swiss brand of chocolate manufactured in the same shape.

Todd AO System of cinema wide screen projection using 65mm film.

toddler's truce The period between 6 and 7pm accepted during the 1950's in Britain as a period when there would be no TV programmes so that mothers could put their children to bed without distraction. Broken in 1957 by the introduction of the BBC *Tonight* programme.

toe mark (USA) Mark on set, usually indicated by crayon or tape, to aid actors to position themselves.

toll TV (USA) Pay TV in which a viewer pays according to the hours actually watched on a metered set.

tone 1. A single frequency sound used to identify sound sources and to line-up sound equipment. **2.** Variations in gradation between black and white or in colours.

tone arm (USA) See **pick-up**.

tone control Electronic circuit for manual control of the frequency response of amplifiers, notably to boost or cut to treble or bass response.

tongue Camera movement combining a crabbing motion of a camera dolly and a panning action on its jib arm.

Tonight BBC Current Affairs programme of the 1960's which pioneered many of the conventions seen in subsequent television magazine programmes.

toning Giving a monochrome picture an overall colour cast, e.g. sepia to simulate early photographs.

top hat 1. Synonym for high hat, a low-level camera mounting. **2.** A top cymbal on a drum kit.

top light Illumination of a subject from overhead.

top shot Shot taken from above.

top-and-tail To write an introduction and pay-off to an almost complete recorded picture story. orded picture story.

toppy Apparently distorted sound with very emphasised treble and too little base. Opposite of **bassy** sound.

Topsy System of electronically grading film prints for television transmission similar to **TARIF**.

tormentor A flat placed between the set and the cyclorama to prevent shooting off.

toupee tape Double-sided adhesive tape used to fix hairpieces, moustaches, etc,.

tower OB scaffolding structure for mounting a camera or lights.

toys Term used by production staff to describe new pieces of engineering equipment with far from obvious utility. That with which engineers may be found at play.

track 1. (noun) Rails used to run a camera dolly. 2. (verb) To move a camera physically during a shot, e.g. track in, track out.

track in/out The physical movement of a camera towards or away from a scene.

track laying The process of matching the sound tracks to the cut picture prior to a dub.

track reader Loudspeaker connected to a sound track on an editing bench.

tracker Member of a camera team who drives a camera crane.

tracking 1. The mechanical movement of the optics inside a zoom lens. 2. The misalignment of camera tubes such that their plane of focus is different in relation to the lens. 3. The path of a pick-up in a sound or video disc following the grooves or the optical recording paths. 4. The following of the video tracks by the video head(s) in a videotape recorder. 5. To move a camera physically on its dolly or mounting. In Britain this refers to a lateral movement; in USA, any move in any direction.

tracking line The rehearsal axis on which a camera dolly moves across a studio floor to achieve a particular shot.

tracking POV See **subjective track**.

tracking shot Shot taken when the camera physically moves on a dolly or pedestal.

trad Abbreviation for **traditional**. A piece of music with no attributable authorship and therefore frequently free from copyright.

traffic (USA) Programme continuity or presentation department.

trail 1. Short publicity announcement, often illustrated by clips from the production. **2.** Identification and protective leader at the end of a feature film.

trajectory Used by VT editors or special effects staff to begin and end the transition of complex picture effects.

tramlining Method used by some production or continuity assistants to mark up shooting scripts or camera scripts where takes, music, etc, are signified by vertical coloured lines drawn down the sides of the page.

tranny Common abbreviation **1.** A photographic transparency. **2.** A transformer. **3.** A transistor radio.

trans-atlantic crane A large film camera mounting.

transcoder Device for converting one colour standard to another on the same line standard, e.g. PAL to SECAM and vice-versa.

transcription 1. Verbatim script of an interview or an originally unscripted programme as transmitted. **2.** A recording of a transmitted programme for repeat or distribution purposes.

transducer Device for converting one source of energy into another.

transfer 1. The process of transferring (or dumping) film to VT for editing or transmission purposes. **2.** The transfer of 1/4-inch sound tapes to sprocketed 16mm magnetic film prior to the film editing process. **3.** Dubbing from one medium to another.

transfer suite Sound dubbing area where location recordings, discs and cassettes can be transferred to magnetic film track.

transformer Device for stepping up or down an AC voltage, e.g. from 240v to 110v.

transient A momentary electrical disturbance which can upset sensitive electronic equipment.

transient sound Brief sharp sound such as the jangle of a bunch of keys.

transistor A device, normally constructed from silicon crystals, used to amplify or switch electrical signals. From trans-resistor.

transition A bridging shot or an optical or musical change used to get from one shot or sequence to another implying a change of time or place. See **bridge**.

translucent Material which transmits light, but which diffuses the light rays so that the source of illumination cannot be discerned.

translucent screen Semi-transparent screen used for the back projection of pictures.

transmission (TX) **1.** The point at which a programme is publicly broadcast. **2.** Any information sent by a transmitter.

transmission copy Final version of a tape or film ready for transmission. See **show print**.

transmitter An apparatus for radiating or distributing signals.

transparency Common term for a photographic slide. Any image to be viewed by transmitted light.

transparent **1.** Allowing the passage of energy without loss or distortion. **2.** Characteristic of electronic equipment in which the output is indistinguishable from the input.

transverse scan recorder See **quad/quadruplex**.

trap A disguised opening for a camera in a set, or a gap in the scenery where the camera may briefly retreat out of another camera's shot.

trapezium Distortion of a video picture resulting in opposite edges of the frame appearing not to be parallel.

travel & duty (T & D) BBC term for reclaimable expenses incurred by individuals as part of their duties.

traveller 1. (USA) A roller caption. **2.** A drape on a cyclorama track, which can be drawn to fill in part of the background of a set.

travelling matte Feature film term for the technique of combining two separately shot images, e.g. a character in the foreground filmed against pictures of an exterior shot elsewhere, for flying sequences, etc.

travelogue Cinema film short evoking faraway places. The style survives on certain travel programmes summed up by the lines *'and as we say farewell, the sun sinks slowly in the West.'*

tray (USA) Horizontally-mounted rotary slide projector magazine.

treads 1. A step-ladder. **2.** A flight of stage steps. **3.** Rostra representing steps or staircases.

treatment The first stage in production, in which the director writes in detail how he intends to shoot a programme with suggestions as to casting, locations, picture sources, etc. Used as a basis for discussion at offers meetings.

tree stand A tube on a stand for mounting vertical objects on a set, like the stand for fake Christmas trees.

tree wing Silhouette cut-outs at the sides of a stage set implying forest, etc.

triax A coaxial cable with an additional screen capable of handling coded commands and power to a camera, as well as receiving video from the camera. Useful for control over long distances.

trim To change the carbon electrodes in an arc-light, a term presumably derived from trim- ming the wick of an oil lamp.

trim bin A large bin surmounted by a crossbar on which film trims are clipped or pinned.

trims Unused pieces of exposed film left over after a final assembly has been made.

Trinicon A TV camera tube used in some single tube colour cameras.

triniscope Method of colour film recording of video images using a red, blue and green projector system directed at a film camera.

Trinitron Colour monitor using a patented single gun display tube and a screen coated in stripes of primary colour instead of dots grouped in triads.

trip switch Automatic circuit breaker, performing the function of a fuse.

triple standard TV equipment capable of working in PAL, SECAM or NTSC standards.

tripod The most common location camera mount, a fluid head mounted on three adjustable legs.

tripod on skid dolly A tripod fixed to a wheel base. See **rolling legs**.

tromboning Common fault of incompetent cameramen who cannot resist repeated zooming in and out of a scene.

trough (USA) A ground row of lights.

trucking (USA) General American term for camera movement which, in the UK, would be described as crabbing or tracking.

T-stop A method of calibration of a lens based on the actual light transmission at various apertures.

tube 1. A valve. **2.** An evacuated glass envelope with an electron gun at one end, either a light sensitive target at the other end (in the case of a camera tube) or a phosphor screen in a display device such as a monitor or oscilloscope.

tubular bar See **hanging iron**.

tum tab A name caption in the lower third of the television screen, unique to Scotland.

tumble The appearance of an image rolling over and over, continuously changing to reveal axis of rotation. Can be done with sophisticated digital video effects.

tungsten Metal used for the filament in most light bulbs which sheds an orange-hued light.

tungsten film Film which is balanced for use in interior light. The usual film used in television.

tungsten light Lighting by incandescent lights with tungsten filaments.

turkey A disastrous programme held up to critical derision or which, in the cinema, is a financial disappointment.

turn over! Instruction given by the director to the cameraman and sound recordist to run their equipment. Only when the cameraman has confirmed with the word '*running!*' and the recordist '*speed!*' will the director call '*action!*' for a shot to begin. In the USA, '*roll!*' is used.

turn-around time 1. The time taken to prepare a studio between two programmes. **2.** The production time between two episodes or two instalments of a regular programme.

turnkey Supply of a complete television studio installation ready for use by a manufacturer or contractor to a production company.

turntable 1. The mechanical transport of a record player. **2.** The mechanism of an animation table that enables graphic rotations of graphics or small three-dimensional objects.

turret Lens mounting in which three or four

prime lenses are mounted on a rotating disc large-ly superseded by the zoom lens.

TV Times British weekly publication, with regional variations, listing programmes pub-lished by the Independent Television Companies.

TV-am English commercial breakfast time television company.

tweak **1.** Fine adjustment of a piece of techni-cal equipment. **2.** Compulsive nervous habit of engineers as in *'it's working perfectly, but I'll just try giving it a tweak'*.

tweaker A small screwdriver concealed by engineers.

tweeter Small high-frequency loudspeaker.

twin filament lamp A lamp containing two filaments within the same bulb, providing the facility of a full or half-power output without a change in the colour temperature.

twin track Recording of different material on two half-tracks of a 1/4-inch sound recorder.

twister (USA) A double-sided light housing in which the same bulb can be used as a soft light or spotlight.

two hander **1.** Magazine programme with two presenters. **2.** A play starring only two actors.

two way (radio) Radio term for **down-the-line**.

two-colour process Early system of colour pro-cessing in which the visible spectrum was split into blue/green and red/orange. Superseded by the red-blue-green, three-colour system.

two-shot A shot containing only two characters.

two-three-two-three scan (USA) NTSC way of showing 24 frames per second on a 60 cycles per second electrical system. PAL and SECAM trans-mit 25 frames per second on a 50-cycle system.

twofer (USA) Cynical description of a studio presenter chosen to placate local groups, who is able to represent by background two or more different political, religious or racial viewpoints. From '*two for the price of one*'.

Tyne Tees Television Commercial television franchise holder for Newcastle or north-eastern England.

typecasting The unfortunate result in the career of a performer who so regularly seen performing near-identical character parts that it becomes impossible for them to be credible in any other kind of role.

U Abbreviation for **upstage**..

U Certificate Old British Board of Film Censors certificate for films deemed suitable for children to watch.

U-format/matic Videotape system using 3/4-inch cassettes.

U/S Abbreviation for **upstage**.

U-wrap The path a video takes around the recording/replay heads.

Uher German make of portable 1/4-inch tape recorder.

ulcer Filter in the form of a perforated board that is placed in front of some of the largest location lights to control their output.

Ulster Television Commercial television contractor for Northern Ireland.

ultra high frequency (UHF) Radio frequency from 300-3000 MHz.

umbrella A folding reflector, usually silver coloured, used to bounce light from lamps or flashguns.

umbrella audience effect Inherited viewing. Audience for a possibly unappealing programme held as a result of popular programming before or immediately after.

unbalanced Applied to audio circuits where the signal is carried on a single conductor with respect to earth.

uncut Processed film or tape prior to editing.

under the line See **below the line**.

under-exposure Production of a dark image lacking detail due to the camera iris being insufficiently open for the available light.

underbridge topper Industrial crane, sometimes used by film crews for difficult shots. Similar to a cherry picker but able to swing its arm below ground level to look under bridges, etc.

undercrank Shooting film at a slower than normal speed so that on projection the action seems to be speeded up.

underground film 1960's term for films made outside the influence of the Hollywood studios commercial cinema and distributors, often of an experimental nature.

underplay To act a role in a low-key manner.

underrun To produce a programme which ends before the planned duration.

undershoot 1. To shoot less than the budgeted or estimated film footage. 2. to finish shooting a scene without getting all the shots necessary for successful editing. 3. A form of distortion of an electronic signal.

understudy An actor who is rehearsed to replace another in an emergency.

underwater blimp A watertight camera housing used in underwater photography.

underwater camera Camera mounted in a pressurised or waterproofed blimp.

uni-directional microphone A microphone which is sensitive to sound only from the front.

unilateral Exclusive use of a satellite telecommunications link by a single broadcasting organisation.

Union des Radiodiffusions et Télévision Nationale Africains (URTNA) Association of African TV companies for training and cultural exchange.

unit 1. A team of technicians. 2. A production team.

unit car A car hired by a location unit for general run-around purposes.

unit manager Official working within a large film unit concerned with administration and finance.

University of the Air Early term for the **Open University**.

unmodulated An electronic signal representing pictures or sound before being combined with a high-frequency carrier wave for coding or transmission.

unsqueezed print Wide-screen film print from an anamorphic negative, corrected for normal projection.

up-front money Finance raised from an outside source to pay for a production before shooting can begin.

up grams/music/tape Gallery director's instruction for the sound supervisor to fade in a music or effects sound track.

upcut (USA) Accidental running together of two successive sound sources through bad editing or sound control in the gallery, e.g. the sound of two people speaking simultaneously despite a clear picture cut.

update 1. Part of a news item which uncovers new aspects in a slowly unfolding continuing story, e.g. a long court case or international conference. **2.** Electronically produced stop frame.

uplink Signal sent by a ground station to a communications satellite for retransmission to receivers on earth.

upper loop The loop of film on a camera or projector between the first sprocket and the gate.

uprating Compensating for poor light by exposing and then specially-processing film as though it was faster than its normal ISO/DIN rating.

upstage 1. (noun) The area of the set furthest from the audience or the cameras. **2.** (verb) to steal the limelight by over-acting and distracting attention from other performers.

upwards conversion Conversion of a picture from a lower to a higher-line standard, e.g. 405 to 625 lines.

utility man Low-ranking member of an American film crew. See **gofer**.

UPSTAGE

V Abbreviation for **volt**.

VCR See **video cassette recorder**.

VDU See **visual display unit**.

VFL See **very low frequency**.

VFX Script abbreviation for **visual effects**. See **special effects**.

VHD See **very high density**.

VHF See **very high frequency**.

VHS See **video home system**.

VI See **volume indicator**.

VITS Vertical interval test signals. See **insertion test signals**.

VLAD See **Vinten low-angle dolly**.

VLP See **videodisc long play**.

VLS See **very long shot**.

VO See **vision operator**.

V/O Script abbreviation for **voice over**.

VOA See **Voice of America**.

VS See **vision supervisor**.

VT See **videotape**.

VT build-up See **videotape build-up**.

VT clock Electronically-generated countdown at the beginning of a VT recording, which serves the same purpose as a front leader in film.

VT editor A technician who edits videotape.

VTR See **videotape recorder**.

VU See **volume unit**.

valve A device for rectifying or amplifying electronic signals consisting of an evacuated glass envelope, a heated cathode that emits a stream of electrons and a number of elements that regulate the flow of electrons. Superseded by the transistor except for specialist and very high-power applications.

vamp 1. An actress portraying a seductive role. 2. Musical improvisation to fill up available time, as in '*vamp till ready*'.

Van Allen belts Ionised layers in the upper atmosphere which reflect radio waves back to earth permitting long-distance radio reception.

variable area Optical sound printing system where the width of exposed film is directly related to the amplitude of the recorded sound.

variable density Optical sound film recording technique where the density of exposure of the sound track is directly related to the amplitude of the recorded sound.

variable focus lens Long-winded name for a **zoom lens**.

variable speed motor Film camera electric motor which enables the cameraman to over or undercrank at will.

Variac Trade name for a transformer with variable output voltage.

Variety Productions specialising in light music, dance and comedy material.

Variety Artistes Federation British trades union for performers in the variety theatre, incorporated in British Actors' Equity.

varispeed 1. A continuously variable speed control over a limited range for an audio tape recorder, usually for pitch control. **2.** (USA) Slow motion or freeze frame facilities on a videotape machine.

vaseline lens shot Petroleum jelly smeared around a camera filter to give a defocused effect around the borders of an image, leaving a clear porthole in the centre. An easy means of achieving a dreamy effect or even of softening the wrinkles on an elderly performer.

Vaudeville (USA) Variety tradition featuring music, dance, and stand-up comedy routines.

vaultmaster (USA) Laboratory or studio supervisor in charge of film stock.

vaults Secure cool area for storing film, so called because early nitrate film was extremely dangerous and had to be stored in vault-like conditions.

vectorscope A special oscilloscope used to display the phase relationship of coded colour signals. Used to line-up colour equipment.

velocillator (USA) A small camera **dolly**.

velours Heavy velvet-type material used for stage curtains.

venue Rendezvous at a location.

vertical hold The adjustment for locking the field scans of a television set or monitor to the incoming signal.

vertical interval The blanking interval between each scan on a video image. Effectively, the same as frame bars on film. Vision mixing and editing equipment is designed to cut during this period to avoid picture disturbance.

vertical resolution The sharpness of a picture in the vertical plane, limited by the number of lines that make up the picture.

very high density (VHD) A videodisc recording system using capacitance instead of grooves.

very high frequency (VHF) Radio waves from 30-300 MHz.

very long shot (VLS) A shot that includes full-length figures and much of the surrounding set, a very wide shot.

very low frequency (VLF) 3-30 kHz radio waves.

video 1. The representation of pictures as an electronic signal. 2. Commonly used term for home video recorders. 3. Light entertainment term for a performance by a music group in which they sing, act and caper to the playback of a commercial recording. Many such videos are actually shot on film.

video artist Creator of artefacts using videotape techniques not intended as broadcast entertainments but as art forms in their own right.

video assist (USA) See **electronic viewfinder**.

video cassette Videotape in a contained cassette form as opposed to open reel-to-reel tape systems.

video cassette recorder (VCR) Obsolete term for a videotape recorder now largely supplanted by terms specifying particular formats; e.g. VHS, U-matic, Beta, low-band, high-band.

video channel The band of transmission frequencies allocated to a programme channel.

video director (USA) Alternative term for a **switcher** or **vision mixer**.

video effect An effect produced electronically as opposed to an effect contrived on the set or location.

video feedback (USA) Vision signal feeding back on itself. Vision equivalent of audio howl around.

video home system (VHS) Format for domestic 1/2-inch videotape recording and playback.

video phase reversal 1. Reversal of an image vertically or horizontally, i.e. providing an upside down or mirror image of a scene. **2.** Electronically providing a negative image of a scene.

video wall Programmed display system in which banks of television monitors are mounted showing pictures either separately or in combination to make one giant composite screen.

videodisc 1. The system of recording broadcast pictures on to a disc to enable replay of still frames, slow-motion, etc. **2.** Optical laser-read replay only disc system.

videodisc long player (VLP) Replay mode for videodisc giving maximum replay time.

videotape Magnetic tape for recording and replaying pictures and sound used in a number of formats 2-inch Quad, 1=inch, 3/4-inch U-matic, 1/2-inch VHS, Betamax, 1/4-inch Quartercam, etc.

videotape build-up System of recording and re-recording over the same background giving a multiple exposure effect, e.g. enabling the same performer to appear as twins in the same scene.

videotape recorder A machine for recording and playing back videotape.

videotext A general term for an alphanumeric or graphic information service, digitally transferred over communications links.

Vidicon A type of camera tube using a photoconductive target. Now largely redundant because of its lag properties.

View-Data A system for distributing written information to a television screen.

viewer **1.** An optical device replicating the camera lens which a director uses to estimate shot sizes and lens effects. Normally worn on a lanyard round the neck. See **Tewe lens**. **2.** An optical device for examining film or slides. **3.** Member of a television audience.

viewer research Audience research.

viewfinder The means by which a cameraman lines up his picture. May be electronic or optical and may or may not look directly through the lens. See **single lens reflex**.

viewing group A select group of people required to watch chosen programmes collectively or at home for audience research purposes.

viewing theatre Projection theatre for viewing rushes, previewing programmes, etc.

viewpoint 1. The position from which a camera observes its subject. **2.** The personal opinion of a contributor or programme maker.

vignette 1. To mask off part of the picture by electronic means or a card cut-out. **2.** A card cut-out, e.g. shaped like a keyhole, placed in front of a camera lens. Sometimes used in the studio in conjunction with colour separation overlay/chromakey.

vignetting Corner shading of a picture due to poor optics or a very wide-angle lens allowing the corners of the lens hood to appear in shot.

Vinten British manufacturer of camera mounting equipment.

vinten low-angle dolly (VLAD) Camera dolly with a short jib arm.

vision control room The technical area in which lighting control and camera matching takes place for an electronic television studio.

vision controller Technician in the gallery or adjacent technical area in charge of monitoring picture quality. See **racks**.

vision mixer 1. The operator in a gallery or scanner who cuts, mixes and creates effects under the instruction of the director during a transmission or recording. **2.** The equipment that enables cuts, mixes and effects between vision sources in a studio or outside broadcast.

vision operator (CVO) Person who operates the camera control unit in the vision area of a studio or outside broadcast.

vision story (USA) News story read directly to camera by the newsreader without film or VT illustration.

vision supervisor (VS) The person who is responsible for operating the lighting console in a BBC studio.

vision switcher

vision switcher (USA) **Vision mixer**, either the equipment or the operative.

vista shot (USA) A very long shot.

Vistavision A wide screen format for the cinema, attempted as early as 1919 using film passed horizontally through the camera instead of vertically, and giving a frame size three times the width of standard 35mm.

visual chewing gum Contemptuous term for the sort of programme whose main purpose is to fill up air time as cheaply as possible between commercials. See **wallpaper**.

VISUAL CHEWING GUM

visual display unit (VDU) Common term for a television screen used with computer terminals, word processors, etc.

visual effects See **special effects.**

visual music (USA) See **foreground music.**

visualisation Process of converting an idea or literary storyline into a screenplay.

visuals Illustrative material in a current affairs story, e.g. a still picture, a slide, film or VT clip connected in some way to the script.

vocals The sung parts of a musical recording.

Vocoder An audio device for breaking up speech into energy bands. Used for special effects.

voice 1. Sound recordist's term for volume of speech as in *'give it more voice'*, i.e. speak louder in front of the microphone. **2.** To read the out-of-vision scripted narration of a programme.

Voice of America (VOA) Government-run external broadcasting service of the United States.

voice of god Gallery talkback which is routed through loudspeakers on the studio floor, instead of through the earphones of the floor manager and camera crew.

voice over (V/O) Narration recorded out-of-vision by a presenter. See **out-of-vision.**

voice track An audio track for speech as distinct from music or effects.

volt Measure of electrical forces.

volume Intensity of sound reproduction.

volume compression Quiet passage amplified and loud passages reduced, to obtain overall even level of audio signal.

volume indicator/VI meter Dial displaying the signal amplitude on a sound recording system.

volume unit meter/VU meter Instrument on a

sound recorder for monitoring the average sound level measured in decibels. Not generally considered suitable for broadcast work, because it may not register transient high-level sounds that may overload equipment.

vox pops (*Vox populi* = the voice of the people). Technique of asking simple questions to random members of the public to get apparently spontaneous reactions. Usually edited thereafter to give an impression of majority endorsement of a viewpoint and to achieve witty juxtapositions of opposed viewpoints.

W /A Script abbreviation for **wide angle**.

wagon/waggon Film studio low-loading transporter for sets.

waist shot (USA) Mid-shot.

wait for a clear! Instruction by a studio director at the end of a recording for everyone to remain on the set until the engineers have checked the quality of the tape.

walk a flat To move a flat by hand in a vertical position from one position to another in a set.

walk-on An artist who is either classified as: **walk on one**, a performer who is directed, but never speaks, or **walk on two**, one who may speak unimportant or unscripted words, normally in a crowd scene. See **extra**.

walk-through Sequential but interrupted rehearsal of a scene for blocking-in shots or practising camera movements.

walkie-looker (USA) Portable video monitor.

walkie-talkie Lightweight two-way radio link.

walking shot 1. A moving shot in which the camera tracks with a moving performer. 2. Static shot in which the performers approach the camera whilst speaking their lines.

wallpaper Film or videotape without sound over which a commentary is read. Much used in news programmes.

waltzing waters Finely-controlled fountains for use in spectacular entertainment shows.

wand A non-functioning prop microphone held as a totem by pop musicians who are miming to their own recordings or used by presenters as a symbol of their authority.

warble tone A frequency-modulated single tone.

Wardour Street Street in Soho, London. The traditional geographical centre of the British feature film industry.

wardrobe 1. Costumes used in a programme. Also called **frocks. 2.** Costume department itself.

wardrobe handler (USA) Wardrobe mistress or assistant to a costume designer.

wardrobe mistress/master Person responsible to the costume designer for the acquisition and maintenance of clothes throughout a production.

warm-up Time spent working up an audience by telling jokes, etc, prior to the recording or live transmission of a programme.

warm-up man Performer, normally a member of the production team, who entertains an invited audience prior to the beginning of an actual recording or transmission by giving a one-man variety performance.

warm-up time Time taken for electronic equipment to be switched on and to heat up to an operational condition.

warning light Red light outside a filming or recording area warning people to stay away or at least be quiet during a take.

wash Painting a thin light-toned coat of paint over a darker background to create shadow effects.

wash-out (USA) Fading to white or bleaching out an image.

washing Final stage in film process, in which remaining chemicals are rinsed from the film.

watershed Concept that programmes transmitted before the middle of the evening are watched by children and should, therefore, be innocuous, whereas material transmitted later can be seen only by adults. See **toddler's truce, adult viewing, family viewing.**

watt Unit of electrical power.

wave form monitor An oscilloscope dedicated to displaying and measuring an electronic signal.

waveband Arbitary division of the electro-magnetic spectrum.

waveform The visual display of a regular electronic signal on an oscilloscope, usually a graphic display of amplitude against time.

waveguide Conductor of microwave signal to or from an aerial.

wavelengths Distance between successive corresponding points on a single-frequency elec-tro-magnetic wave or sound wave.

weaving A projector fault resulting in the film shifting laterally on the screen.

wedges Rectangular blocks of wood sawn diagonally to make equal wedges, used in vari-ous combinations by grips to support camera dolly rails on uneven ground.

weighting Artificial bias applied to audio sig-nal when carrying out noise measurements, etc.

Wembley mount Robust outside broadcast camera mount.

Westrex Manufacturer of television sound and replay equipment.

Westward TV Commercial company which once held the franchise for SW England from Plymouth. Replaced by Television South West (TSW).

wet finger job A guessed-at camera exposure without recourse to an exposure meter.

wet gate projector/printer Film projection system in which the film passes a lubricated gate instead of being played through a pressure plate. Used to minimise the risk of scratches.

wet hire Hire of technical equipment complete with operational personnel. Opposite of **dry hire**.

wet string A single video or sound cable link between two pieces of equipment.

whip pan Extremely fast camera pan from one object to another. Also called **zip pan**.

white balance An automatic line-up facility on some video cameras that provides correct colour rendition of a scene by equalising the red, green and blue components reflected from a white object. If white is correct, then all other colours are assumed to be correct.

white clipping Artificial limiting of maximum amplitude of video signal.

white crushing/compression Loss of light tones in an electronic picture due to over-exposure.

white edging The outlining of a dark lettering or object in white, either deliberately to achieve prominence, or as a result of a camera fault.

white infinity Combination of a brightly-lit white cyclorama and white floor paint, usually with some electronic manipulation of the picture to create an impression of a performance taking place in infinite space.

white noise Random sound spread evenly throughout the spectrum usually heard as a hiss.

whodunnit Obsolete term for a mystery or detective film.

wide screen Any projection screen with an aspect ratio wider than the standard academy frame of 1.33 : 1 aspect ratio. See **Vistavision**, **Cinemascope**.

wide shot A loosely-used term for a shot taking in a panoramic view.

wide-angle lens Any lens giving an angle of view wider than the normal focused area of human vision, e.g. less than a 25mm lens on a 16mm camera and more than 35° on a video lens.

wig A hairpiece.

wigwag (USA) Flashing red lights outside a studio denoting that filming is taking place.

wild motor A variable-speed motor for a film camera which enables the cameraman to over or undercrank.

wild reel (USA) News story kept on a separate reel from a compilation of stories in sequence which may be inserted at any point in a live show.

wild sound Background atmospheric sound recorded on a different microphone from a commentary track, e.g. crowd noises at a sporting event.

wild track 1. Background effects recorded non-synchronously by a sound recordist on location to assist the editing. 2. Non-synchronous speech out-of-vision.

wild walls (USA) See **breakthrough piece**.

wind machine Large fan used to create artificial wind.

wind shield See **wind gag**.

wind-up! Instruction given to a floor manager by the director usually 15 seconds before the end of an interview and communicated to an interviewer by a slowly-rotating hand gesture.

winder Geared mechanism for winding film spools.

windgag Cover or blimp fitted over a microphone on location to cut out wind and rain noise.

window Visual electronic effect in the form of 1. The box printed over a videotape picture which displays the time code numbers. 2. A frozen box wipe on the vision mixer. 3. Available satellite time.

wing Flat on the side of a set to mask a background or to prevent shooting off.

wing it To improvise wildly because of unforeseen events. See **busk it**, **Murphy's law**.

wings Areas either side of a proscenium which are concealed from the audience by drapes or flats. Also used loosely for the sides of a studio set out of shot.

wipe 1. To erase a recording. 2. Electronic means of getting from one picture to another where the one appears to wipe the other off the window or screen.

wipe in To bring a new picture into shot by means of a wipe.

wipe out To lose a picture by wiping to black.

wire 1. Teleprinter or facsimile system. 2. An individual strand of cable.

wireless mike A radio microphone.

wireman An electrician mainly concerned with installation work.

wobble device Electronic effect which puts a wobble effect on a picture, e.g. to simulate a drunk's point of view.

wobblyscope/wobblevision Poor hand-held camerawork.

woofer 1. Low-frequency loudspeaker, usually used with a tweeter or high-frequency speaker. 2. Compressed air mortar used to simulate explosions, so named as it makes things go *'woof'*.

word cue 1. Rehearsed word or phrase in a script signalling another sequence or action to begin. 2. Presenter or actor's cue taken entirely from a script or from the sense of a recorded speech.

work on off-duty days (WOODS) BBC term for a system of payment for working on off-duty days.

work print Alternative name for a film **cutting copy**.

work to camera one!/ two!/ three! Director's or floor manager's instruction to performers to address a designated camera which is live.

working title Temporary descriptive title given to a production from its inception, but not necessarily the one which will finally appear on screen or on publicity material.

World Radio TV Handbook Annual publication listing essential information about all overseas broadcasting organisations.

World Service BBC radio service transmitted worldwide in English from Bush House, London.

World Television Service Worldwide television news broadcasting by satellite developed from the radio World Service of the BBC.

Worldwide Television News Television news agency partly owned by British Independent Television News.

wow A variation of pitch on recorded sound normally caused by faulty speed in the tape transport or by stretched tape. Describes variations between 1 and 10 times per second.

wrap **1.** Director's instruction to the crew that the day's shoot is finished. **2.** VT description of way in which tape is coiled around a video drum in different tape formats, e.g. 'A' wrap or 'B' wrap.

Wratten filter Filters manufactured by Kodak used to colour-correct daylight film used in tungsten light conditions, etc.

Writers' Guild of Great Britain Union for professional scriptwriters.

Wurmser Graphic design company, specifically a system of animation in which card cutouts are manipulated in front of electronic cameras for simple graphics, etc.

X Script abbreviation for **crosses**, e.g. XL = crosses to camera left. **X/F** Script abbreviation for **cross-fade**.

XLR A style of professional audio connector.

Xenon lamp Intense lamp used on film projectors, using an arc light in a quartz envelope containing xenon gas under high pressure.

X-movie Film deemed by all British Board of Film Censors to be too horrific or salacious to be seen by anyone under the age of 16 — now generally used to describe any horror or sex film.

XY zoom Device used to focus on part of a film as it goes through the gate, thus allowing a close-up or a zoom out from a detail in the film.

Y Engineering abbreviation for luminance. **yashmak** Diffuser for a lamp which only masks the lower portion of the beam.

yoke Set of electro-magnetic coils mounted around a cathode-ray tube to direct the electron beam.

Yorkshire Television Commercial television company with the IBA for the Yorkshire region.

Zap/zapping To switch rapidly between channels on a home TV receiver by using a remote control device.

Zeiss German manufacturer of lenses.

zero level The average level for sound and the level used to line-up sound equipment (0.775 volt into a 600 ohm load).

zip pan Fast lateral camera movement from one image to another. Also called a **whip pan**.

zipped characters Captions, normally lower third names or subtitles, which appear letter by letter as in typewriting. See also **crawl**.

zones Defined areas of TV picture, indicating the areas of maximum and minimum viewer's perception.

zoom in/out To go closer or further from a part of an image using the zoom control on a camera lens.

zoom lens A lens with an infinite number of variable focal lengths, which can widen and narrow the angle of view in vision. The usual lens on electronic cameras.

zoom mike (USA) Directional microphone with an adjustable angle of sound sensitivity used as a single all-purpose microphone when the cameraman operates without a recordist on news reports.

zoom stand Vertical mount for an animation camera.

NOTES

NOTES

NOTES

NOTES

NOTES

NOTES

NOTES